continued on back

The Analysis of Cross-tabulated Data

The Analysis of Cross-tabulated Data

GRAHAM J. G. UPTON

Lecturer in Mathematics
University of Essex

JOHN WILEY & SONS
Chichester · New York · Brisbane · Toronto

Library of Congress Cataloging in Publication Data:
Upton, Graham J. G.
  The analysis of cross-tabulated data.

Includes index.
  1. Contingency tables. I. Title.

QA 277.U67   519.5'3   78-4120
ISBN 0 471 99659 9

Printed by J. W. Arrowsmith Ltd., Bristol BS3 2NT

To M and D

Preface

This book arose out of a lecture course which I was invited to give at the Summer School of the European Consortium for Political Research at the University of Essex in 1976. In preparing my notes for this course it quickly became apparent that there had been enormous strides in the development of the analysis of cross-tabulated data in the years since 1970 and that there was no simple introductory guide to the new methods. My colleagues at the Summer School welcomed my notes enthusiastically and the idea of this book was born.

The intention of this book is to provide an introduction to the complexities of the analysis of cross-classified data of the type known to the statistician as a contingency table and to the social scientist as a cross-tabulation. The book is aimed primarily at the social science research worker who has collected his data and must now analyse them. With multivariable data he has in the past conducted the analysis in terms of measures of association for two-way tables; armed with this book he should be able to contemplate a more subtle analysis.

The book contains a profusion of references to the source papers; the notation used is intended to match that of the source papers as far as is practicable. A general familiarity with basic statistical methodology is all that is required of the reader, and the book should therefore prove equally useful as a methods text, both for the research worker and for students taking advanced statistics courses.

Chapter 1 outlines the general problem and provides brief reminders of the essential statistical techniques. Chapters 2 to 4 are concerned with a résumé of the more useful of the 'traditional' methods of analysis, in particular with methods of association. These chapters also provide an introduction to the use of the log-linear model, which is discussed at length in Chapters 5 to 9. The final chapter is concerned with the special problems associated with panel data. The principal theme of the book is the central importance of the log-linear model and the associated techniques in the analysis of cross-tabulated data.

So far as possible, equations have been included only when they are of material help in understanding the techniques being described. Whenever the theory becomes difficult (for the author as well as the reader!) it has been omitted and replaced by a reference to the source paper and a brief summary.

My thanks are due to many people for making this book possible: to Ivor Crewe for the original Summer School invitation, to Jim Alt for his help in understanding and implementing the computer routine ECTA, to David Robertson for supplying data on the 1975 referendum survey, and to various other colleagues for useful discussions. In particular, I am greatly indebted to my wife for living through the production stages with reasonable tolerance, to my children for not interrupting too often, and to Pat Reader for a magnificent piece of typing.

Any errors that remain in the book are my responsibility alone, and I would appreciate their being brought to my notice.

G. J. G. U.

August 1977

Contents

Appendixes

CHAPTER I

Some Statistical Preliminaries

1.1. INTRODUCTION

This book is concerned with the methods available for the analysis of data of a very particular type. These data consist of *counts* of people, places, or things which have various combinations of characteristics. Such data arise naturally when summarizing surveys and analysing the results of questionnaires, and are very familiar to the quantitative social scientist. Table 1.1 illustrates the summary data for a fictitious survey purportedly concerned with the sporting interests of the British public.

Table 1.1. Results of sporting interest survey

Category of response	Number
Men, over 45, preferring cricket to tennis	58
Men, over 45, preferring tennis to cricket	24
Men, 45 and under, preferring cricket to tennis	74
Men, 45 and under, preferring tennis to cricket	38
Women, over 45, preferring cricket to tennis	12
Women, over 45, preferring tennis to cricket	86
Women, 45 and under, preferring cricket to tennis	13
Women, 45 and under, preferring tennis to cricket	95

The people in this survey have been classified using three criteria: their sex, their age, and their sport preference. Since all three classifications are being utilized simultaneously we speak of the data as having been *cross-classified*. Alternatively, since each of the people in the survey belongs to one of the eight categories in the table, we may refer to the data as *categorical data*.

If we look closely at the numbers in Table 1.1 we notice various characteristics which we can interpret. Most noticeable is that the majority of women prefer tennis (181 out of 206), whereas the majority of men prefer cricket (132 out of 194). Probably the next most obvious characteristics are the domination of the sample by the young (55 per cent. aged 45 and under) and the female majority in those over 45 (98 our of 180 equals 54 per cent.). There are other differences too—the purpose of this book is to describe techniques which will help to show up the interesting features of data of this type.

1.2. CROSS-TABULATION

Cross-tabulation is a word familiar to users of the computer package SPSS (Statistical Package for the Social Sciences)—Nie *et al.* (1975). It refers quite simply to the presentation of the Table 1.1 data in the more succinct form shown in Table 1.2.

Table 1.2. Cross-tabulation of Table 1.1 data

	Men				Women		
Preference	Over 45	45 and under	*Total*	*Preference*	Over 45	45 and under	*Total*
Cricket	58	74	132	Cricket	12	13	25
Tennis	24	38	62	Tennis	86	95	181
Total	82	112	194	*Total*	98	108	206

We can refer to the two halves of Table 1.2 as two subtables. Each subtable involves the two criteria age and sport preference, and for this reason we refer to such a table as a *two-way* table. Alternatively, since the subtable is easily written in two dimensions and consists of an array of numbers, it may also be referred to as a *two-dimensional array* or *two-dimensional table*. The complete table, on the other hand, can only be represented easily in two dimensions by being broken up and presented as shown in Table 1.2. The primary break was sex for Table 1.2, and we could equally well have sub-divided by, for example, age, as shown in Table 1.3.

Table 1.3. Alternative presentation of Table 1.2

	Over 45				45 and under		
Preference	Men	Women	*Total*	*Preference*	Men	Women	*Total*
Cricket	58	12	70	Cricket	74	13	87
Tennis	24	86	110	Tennis	38	95	133
Total	82	98	180	*Total*	112	108	220

Both Tables 1.2 and 1.3 are really two alternative two-dimensional representations of the three-dimensional table shown as Table 1.4. In effect Table 1.4 shows a symmetrical arrangement of Table 1.1 which does not emphasize one set of interlinkages at the expense of others. For this reason it

Table 1.4. Three-dimensional arrangement of Table 1.2

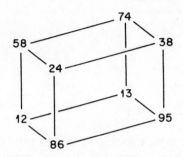

may be preferable to the representations of Tables 1.2 and 1.3, but of course it is not a really practicable method of writing data.

Later we shall learn how to handle the analysis of three-dimensional data such as those in Table 1.1 and, indeed, will discover that the techniques can equally well be applied to n-dimensional ($n > 3$) data.

1.3. SAMPLES, POPULATIONS, AND RANDOM VARIATION

In Table 1.1 we showed a hypothetical set of survey results. We can trace the history of these results back to an original set of instructions given to the survey team, which we can presume to have been, in essence, something like 'Go out and interview 400 adults, selecting your interviewees according to the following rules . . .'. If the sampling rules were sound, then the results obtained in the sample can be expected to mirror the population as a whole. What population this is depends on the sampling instructions. For example, if all the interviews were conducted in Greater London between 10 a.m. and 11 a.m. on Friday 22nd July 1977, then the results, strictly speaking, constitute a sample from the population of people available for interview at that place at that time. If this population is of very much the same type (with respect to the attributes age, sex, and cricket/tennis preference) as the remainder of the population of Great Britain then—but only then—could we reasonably claim to have drawn our sample from the population of Great Britain. It is very difficult to sample a heterogeneous population, and details of possible techniques lie outside the scope of this book. The interested reader is referred to Cochran (1963).

The characteristic of samples, of course, is that we cannot expect exactly the same numbers to appear every time we take a sample. For instance, if a second survey team used the same sampling techniques as the first, then it would interview a different sample of people and might obtain aggregate results such as those given in Table 1.5. These results are superficially rather different to those in Table 1.3, but on closer inspection the same broad

Table 1.5. Results of the second survey team

	Over 45				45 and under		
Preference	Men	Women	Total	Preference	Men	Women	Total
Cricket	53	20	73	Cricket	68	11	79
Tennis	25	76	101	Tennis	36	111	147
Total	78	96	174	Total	104	122	226

preferences—cricket for men, tennis for women—can be seen. The important point is that *just by chance there can be considerable variations between samples*; we refer to it as *random sampling variation*. The corollary, of course, is that we must not believe that our sample *exactly* mirrors the population.

1.4. THE NORMAL DISTRIBUTION

There is a very important theorem in statistics, called the *central limit theorem*, which states *inter alia* that any quantity which is in essence a total of a number of similar individual units will have approximately a normal distribution. Because we are so often implicitly dealing with totals, the normal distribution is of considerable importance in statistics. Of particular importance is the so-called *unit normal* distribution, which refers to the special case of a normal distribution with mean 0 and variance 1.

If X is a random variable having a unit normal distribution then we define

$$P[X \le x] = \Phi(x) \tag{1.1}$$

where the left-hand side of equation (1.1) reads 'the probability that the random variable X takes values less than or equal to x'. The unit normal distribution is symmetrical about the mean, 0, and hence we have the identity

$$\Phi(-x) = 1 - \Phi(x) \tag{1.2}$$

Appendix 1 provides abbreviated tables of the value of $\Phi(x)$ for a range of positive values of x. For negative values of x the relation (1.2) can be used.

Example 1.1

The random variable X is known to have a unit normal distribution. Suppose that we are interested in the questions:
    (a) What is the probability that X exceeds 0.4?
    (b) Is the value -1.8 unusually small?
    We consult Appendix 1. Corresponding to $x = 0.4$ we find $\Phi(0.4) = 0.655$. This is the probability that X is less than 0.4 and so the required probability is $1 - 0.655 = 0.345$.

Corresponding to $x = 1.8$ we find $\Phi(1.8) = 0.964$. We are interested in $P[X \leq -1.8]$, which by symmetry is equal to $P[X \geq 1.8]$, and is therefore $1 - 0.964 = 0.036$ or 3.6 per cent. We might well feel that -1.8 was indeed a rather small value.

1.5. THE CHI-SQUARED DISTRIBUTION

A second probability distribution, of paramount importance in the study of cross-classified data, is the chi-squared (χ^2) distribution which is related to the normal distribution in the following way. If X has a unit normal distribution, then X^2 has a χ^2 distribution with parameter 1. There is a whole family of X^2 distributions whose form depends on the value of the parameter which is called the 'degrees of freedom'.

If a random variable Y has a χ^2 distribution with d degrees of freedom, we write that Y has a χ_d^2 distribution. In Appendix 2, the values of y are given corresponding to $P[Y > y] = 0.10, 0.05, 0.01,$ and 0.001, for a range of values of d. The examples that follow will illustrate the use of the tables.

The χ^2 distribution has various interesting and useful properties. For example, if Y and Z are independent random variables with χ_d^2 and χ_e^2 distributions respectively, then $(Y + Z)$ has a χ_{d+e}^2 distribution. A second useful *aide memoire* is that the mean of a χ_d^2 distribution is d.

Further details of the χ^2 and normal distributions are given in most introductory statistical texts; see, for example, Yeomans (1968). More extensive tables of both the χ^2 and normal distributions are available in many collections of mathematical tables; see, for example, Lindley and Miller (1952).

Example 1.2

Y is known to have a χ_4^2 distribution. A value of 12.40 is observed. Is this an unusually large value?

We consult Appendix 2 and choose the row corresponding to $d = 4$. We see that $P[Y > 9.49] = 0.05$ and that $P[Y > 13.28] = 0.01$. The value of interest, 12.40, lies between 9.49 and 13.28 and so we may deduce that $P[Y > 12.40]$ lies between 0.05 and 0.01. A probability of between 5 and 1 per cent. is rather small and we would probably feel that 12.40 was a rather large value.

Example 1.3

Y is known to have a χ_{36}^2 distribution. A value of 44.00 is observed. Is this an unusually large value?

We consult Appendix 2 and discover that the values for $d = 36$ are not tabulated. However, the values for $d = 30$ and $d = 40$ are present and using linear interpolation we deduce that the value of y corresponding to $P[Y >$

$y] = 0.10$ is about $40.26 + 0.6 \ (51.81 - 40.26) = 47.19$. Our value, 44.00, is appreciably less than 47.19, which implies $P[Y > 44.00] > 0.10$—more than 10 per cent. of the time we can expect values of Y as large or larger than 44.00, and we therefore conclude that the value of 44.00 is not unusually large.

1.6. TESTING A HYPOTHESIS

Throughout the remainder of the book we shall constantly be making suggestions concerning possible mathematical descriptions of the interrelations present in the data. Such a suggestion is termed a *hypothesis*, and the most familiar of the hypotheses which we shall make concerning a set of data such as that in Table 1.1 is that the characteristics concerned (in that case age, sex, and cricket/tennis preference) are unrelated to one another; this is the hypothesis of mutual independence which we shall study in detail later. We call our primary hypothesis the *null hypothesis*.

To test the truth, or otherwise, of a hypothesis we need to contrast it with some *alternative hypothesis*, which for the cases that we shall consider can be most simply stated as 'the null hypothesis is not true'.

To test the credibility of a null hypothesis, statisticians adopt the following approach. They first assume that the null hypothesis is true. With this assumption they are then able to calculate the probabilities associated with the possible values of some appropriate combination of the numbers under scrutiny. This 'appropriate combination' is called the *test statistic*. If the actual value of the test statistic is unusual—in the sense that, for example, only 1 per cent. of the time would it be expected to take this observed value or a value more extremely different from its average value—then the statistician argues that either he has chanced upon an unusual occurrence or that his original assumption (the null hypothesis) is incorrect. In general, he then prefers to take the latter view and rejects the null hypothesis in favour of the alternative hypothesis.

An example of a hypothesis test is the chi-squared goodness-of-fit test, described in Section 1.8.

1.7. ESTIMATION AND EXPECTATION

One of the features of the data in Table 1.1 was that there were 194 men and 206 women among the 400 interviewees. If the group of people interviewed constituted a random sample from the population of Great Britain, as we shall presume, then we can use the information provided by the sample to draw some conclusions about the population as a whole; this is called *statistical inference*.

Common sense tells us that, if we have no information other than these figures concerning the proportion of men in the population, then our best guess of that proportion would be $194/400 = 0.485$. Common sense on this occasion agrees with a statistical principle. If we call the unknown proportion of men in the population p, then it is quite easy to show that the value of p which makes the observed numbers (194 men and 206 women) most likely to re-occur in a second sample is 0.485; statisticians refer to this value of p as the *maximum likelihood estimate* of p and denote it by $\hat{p}$.

The word 'estimation', therefore, is associated with an inference from the sample about the population. Expectation, on the other hand, is in a sense associated with a move in the opposite direction, as is most easily seen by an example. Suppose that we have a coin which is in mint condition, with 'heads' on one side and 'tails' on the other side. If we are able to toss the coin in a fair manner then everyone will agree that about half the time the coin will come down heads and about half the time it will come down tails. If we toss the coin a total of N times then the statistical expectation of the number of heads will be precisely $\frac{1}{2}N$. Notice that if N is odd then this will not be a whole number—there is no obligation on an *expected frequency* (*expectation*) being a whole number and the terminology leads to some confusion.

We are now in a position to combine the ideas of estimation and expectation together. Let us suppose that we are about to draw a further sample from the population of Great Britain. This time there will be 1000 people in the sample. What is the expectation, based on our previous results, of the number of men in the sample? We start with our estimate of 0.485 for the proportion of men in the population. Using the expected frequency approach it follows that we 'expect' $1000 \times 0.485 = 485$ men. What we are really saying is that if we had to name a single number then it would be 485, and we presume that the number that turns up will be close to this figure. If it is not close to this figure then that implies that our null hypothesis (in this case, that the proportion of men is 0.485) may be incorrect. To test the correctness, or otherwise, of our null hypothesis we require a test statistic, and this takes us to the following section.

1.8. THE CHI-SQUARED GOODNESS-OF-FIT TEST

In the previous section, we discussed a situation in which on the basis of past information we decided that the most likely value for a particular frequency was 485; that is we had an expected frequency of 485. Let us suppose that the observed value of this frequency turns out to be 510. We want to know whether the difference between 510 and 485, 25, is so large that it casts substantial doubt on the line of reasoning which led us to 'expect' the value 485. Clearly the difference, 25, must play a vital role in our decision, and equally clearly we must take into account the relative sizes of the difference

25 and the expected value 485, since 25 will be more significant for small expected values than it is for large expected values. These arguments lead us towards using the quantity $25 \times 25/485$ as a test measure of the satisfactoriness, or otherwise, of our hypothesis.

In the cases that we shall be considering in this book, essentially the same ideas of estimation and expectation will be used to arrive at expected values for each of the individual figures in a cross-classification such as that of Table 1.5. For example, for those data, we might entertain one of the following hypotheses:

H_0' There are equal numbers of men and women in the population, 40 per cent. of both sexes are aged over 45, 3 out of 4 men prefer cricket, and 3 out of 4 women prefer tennis.

H_0'' The results of the second survey team should be the same as those of the first survey team (Table 1.3), except for differences due to random variation.

H_0''' The proportion of men, cricket-lovers, and people aged over 45 are as indicated by the sample, and these three are independent of one another.

For each of these null hypotheses there is an alternative hypothesis which simply states that the null hypothesis is incorrect.

Since we are interested in each of the individual values in the cross-tabulation, we need to combine the information about the differences between the expected values (which we shall denote by E) and the observed values (O). Our earlier reasoning led us to consider the quantity $(O-E)^2/E$, and, on working out some of the statistical theory for this quantity, it turns out that the appropriate method of combining the information is by evaluating this quantity for each cell and then summing over the cells. In other words, our test statistic, denoted by X^2, is defined by

$$X^2 = \sum_{\text{all cells}} \frac{(O-E)^2}{E} \tag{1.3}$$

It was Pearson (1904) who first suggested this test, and he showed that, providing none of the expected values were very small, the distribution of X^2 is approximately χ^2. The degrees of freedom of the χ^2 distribution are given by calculating the value d, where

$$d = (\text{number of cells}) - (\text{number of constraints implied by the data}) \tag{1.4}$$

For the hypotheses H_0' and H_0'' there is only one constraint implied by the data—namely that the expected values total to 400 (the sum of the observed values). For H_0''' the constraints are more complicated and we shall consider hypotheses of this type in more detail later. The quantity X^2 is sometimes referred to as the *Pearson χ^2* test.

An alternative to X^2, of which we shall make extensive use, is the quantity

$$Y^2 = 2 \sum_{\text{all cells}} O \log_e \left(\frac{O}{E}\right) \qquad (1.5)$$

This quantity arises from comparing the estimated joint probability of occurrence of the data under the conditions specified by the null hypothesis with the corresponding probability for the alternative hypothesis. An estimated joint probability of this type is called a likelihood, and equation (1.5) represents a ratio of two likelihoods. Since Y^2 turns out also to have an approximate X^2 distribution, with the same degrees of freedom as X^2, Y^2 is sometimes referred to as the *likelihood ratio* χ^2. In practice there is seldom any great difference between the values of X^2 and Y^2.

Example 1.4

Consider the null hypothesis H_0'. This implies an expectation of 200 men and 200 women, of whom 80 of each will be over 45. Since, according to H_0', 3 out of 4 men prefer cricket, the hypothesis leads to an expected value of $\frac{3}{4} \times 80 = 60$ men over 45 who prefer cricket. The entire set of expected values is given in Table 1.6.

Table 1.6. *Expected frequencies under H_0'*

Preference	Over 45			Preference	45 and under		
	Men	Women	Total		Men	Women	Total
Cricket	60	20	80	Cricket	90	30	120
Tennis	20	60	80	Tennis	30	90	120
Total	80	80	160	Total	120	120	240

Comparing Table 1.6 with the observed values in Table 1.5 we compute

$$X^2 = \frac{(53-60)^2}{60} + \frac{(20-20)^2}{20} + \frac{(25-20)^2}{20} + \cdots + \frac{(111-90)^2}{90}$$

$$= 0.817 + 0.000 + 1.250 + \cdots + 4.900$$

$$= 29.845$$

The degrees of freedom for X^2 are $(8-1) = 7$. Under the assumption that H_0' is correct we have observed a value of 29.845 from a χ_7^2 distribution. We now enquire whether this is a typical value of the χ_7^2 distribution by reference to the tables of χ^2 distributions. In Appendix 2 we see that on only 0.1 per cent. of occasions would we expect to encounter a value of 24.32 or more.

Our observed χ^2 value is considerably larger than 24.32, which makes it even further from the typical value (about 7 for χ_7^2). There is less than a 0.1 per cent. chance of observing by chance a value from a χ_7^2 distribution equal or greater than 29.845, and in consequence we conclude that H_0' is incorrect.

The corresponding value of Y^2 is 33.43 and again we conclude that we must reject H_0'.

Example 1.5

Consider the null hypothesis H_0''. The expected values for the second survey under this hypothesis are those actually obtained by the first survey which were given in Table 1.3. For this hypothesis we therefore compare Tables 1.3 and 1.5 and calculate

$$X^2 = \frac{(53-58)^2}{58} + \frac{(20-12)^2}{12} + \frac{(25-24)^2}{24} + \cdots + \frac{(111-95)^2}{95}$$

$$= 0.431 + 5.333 + 0.042 + \cdots + 2.695$$

$$= 10.563$$

The corresponding value of Y^2 is 9.616. We compare these values with the percentage points of χ_7^2 given in Appendix 2. We see that on 10 per cent of occasions we could expect by chance to observe a value as large or larger than 12.02. Neither the X^2 nor the Y^2 value is as large as 12.02—in other words, these values are typical of those that might be expected and we can accept H_0''. We conclude that the differences in the results obtained by the two surveys are no more than might be expected from random variation.

CHAPTER 2

Association and Independence
in 2 × 2 Tables

2.1. THE BASIC 2×2 TABLE

In the social sciences, data are typically collected, either by interview or by questionnaire, on a great many different topics simultaneously. We may, for example, as part of a single interview, note, for a randomly chosen interviewee, the person's sex, political allegiance, social class, and views on a great number of topics of current interest. All these data can be compactly coded and punched on computer cards, and thence stored on a magnetic tape in an archive. The collection of data of this type is notoriously tricky, and we are not concerned here with how the data were obtained but with their subsequent analysis.

The usual practice of the data analyst faced with this immensely complicated set of data, ranging over perhaps 1000 respondents and 100 questions, has been to study the variables involved two at a time in an effort to determine associations between them. For example, social class and political allegiance are usually found to be strongly allied. As we shall see in later chapters, the recent great strides in the theory of log-linear models imply that (at least in theory) we can handle any number of variables simultaneously—though there may be practical difficulties in interpreting the results! For the present, however, we confine ourselves to two variables, which we shall refer to as A and B, and we suppose that both variables are dichotomous, their categories being designated by A_1 and A_2 and by B_1 and B_2 respectively.

We therefore have four distinguishable types of respondents: those that fall in categories (A_1, B_1), (A_1, B_2), (A_2, B_1), or $(A_2. B_2)$. We now define f_{ij} to be the observed frequency of the respondents who fall into the category (A_i, B_j). We can display these frequencies as shown in Table 2.1.

Table 2.1. Frequency table for 2 × 2 data

	B_1	B_2	Total
A_2	f_{11}	f_{12}	f_{10}
A_2	f_{21}	f_{22}	f_{20}
Total	f_{01}	f_{02}	f_{00}

11

In the table we have introduced some notation for totals. The symbol f_{i0} stands for the (marginal) total of all the respondents who are in category A_i and, similarly, f_{0j} is the total of all those in category B_j, while f_{00} is the grand total of all the cases being considered. Mathematically:

$$f_{i0} = \sum_j f_{ij} \qquad f_{0j} = \sum_i f_{ij} \qquad f_{00} = \sum_i f_{i0} = \sum_j f_{0j} = \sum_i \sum_j f_{ij} \qquad (2.1)$$

2.2. STRUCTURE OF THE TABLE

A table of frequencies such as Table 2.1 can arise in a number of quite distinct ways. For example:

I   We interview f_{00} people and classify them according to their responses to two questions A and B.

II   We interview f_{10} men and f_{20} women and classify them according to their responses to a single question (B).

These two situations are evidently somewhat different and lead initially to quite different approaches to the statistical data analysis. However, as it turns out, the best techniques for handling the data are in general the same for both situations. For a detailed account see Kendall and Stuart (1973).

Interpretation of the results of an analysis may well be affected by the manner in which the data arose. For example, if we deliberately interview twice as many women as men (for whatever reason!) then we would not consider this imbalance significant during our statistical analysis.

For the 2×2 situation there are two principal questions that we can pose concerning the data: first, are the variables A and B related to one another, or are they independent; and second, if they are *not* independent then to what extent are they related? We shall start by considering methods for testing the independence of A and B.

2.3. TESTING FOR INDEPENDENCE OF A AND B

Our natural first question when presented with a 2×2 table of frequencies relating to two variables A and B is 'Is there a pattern?', by which we mean to enquire whether A and B are related in some fashion. If there is no relation between A and B then this means that knowledge concerning the A category of a respondent does not give us information concerning the B category. For example, we are unlikely to be helped in guessing the sex of a respondent by knowing that he or she is under 40. Although it is rather difficult to find variables that are completely unrelated, the idea of independence (no relation) is very important theoretically, and, in mathematical terms, we can expect that, if A and B are independent, then the ratio f_{11}/f_{01} will be roughly equal to f_{12}/f_{02} and f_{11}/f_{10} will be roughly equal to f_{21}/f_{20}.

Even if A and B are completely unrelated it is unlikely that this independence will show up in the $\{f_{ij}\}$, because random variation will probably mess things up. We therefore need a means of testing for independence, and to develop such a test we must go back to the theoretical underlying (bivariate) distribution and develop some more notation.

Table 2.2. Theoretical probability distribution for 2×2 data

	B_1	B_2	Total
A_1	p_{11}	p_{12}	p_{10}
A_2	p_{21}	p_{22}	p_{20}
Total	p_{01}	p_{02}	p_{00}

Write p_{ij} to be the theoretical probability of a randomly chosen respondent belonging to cell (i, j), that is to categories A_i and B_j. We can represent the $\{p_{ij}\}$ in a table (Table 2.2) corresponding to Table 2.1 which gave the observed frequencies. The zero suffixes work as before, so that

$$p_{0j} = \sum_i p_{ij} \qquad p_{i0} = \sum_j p_{ij} \qquad p_{00} = \sum_i \sum_j p_{ij} = 1 \qquad (2.2)$$

The equations (2.2) are direct analogies of the earlier frequency equations (2.1). Note that the total probability p_{00} is, of course, equal to 1, since a respondent must belong to one of the four cells.

If A and B are independent then we would expect that the proportion of those in the B_1 category who were also in the A_1 category would be the same as the proportion of those in the B_2 category who were also in the A_1 category. That is we would require that

$$\frac{p_{11}}{p_{01}} = \frac{p_{12}}{p_{02}} = \frac{p_{10}}{p_{00}} = p_{10}$$

that is

$$p_{11} = p_{10} p_{01} \qquad (2.3)$$

Equivalently, the conditional proportion of those in category B_1 should be unaffected by their A category, that is

$$\frac{p_{11}}{p_{10}} = \frac{p_{21}}{p_{20}} = p_{01}$$

that is

$$p_{11} = p_{01} p_{10} \qquad (2.4)$$

Since the relations (2.3) and (2.4) are the same, the equivalence of the verbal relations is established and we can make the general statement that, if A and B are independent, then

$$p_{ij} = p_{i0}p_{0j} \qquad i, j = 1, 2 \qquad (2.5)$$

We have also seen that, if A and B are independent, then

$$\frac{p_{11}}{p_{01}} = \frac{p_{12}}{p_{02}}$$

and, on cross-multiplying, we obtain

$$p_{11}(p_{12} + p_{22}) = p_{12}(p_{11} + p_{21})$$

so that

$$\frac{p_{11}p_{22}}{p_{12}p_{21}} = 1 \qquad (2.6)$$

is the general relation involving all four cell probabilities.

The quantitity p_{11}/p_{21} can be described as the *odds* on a category A_1 response (rather than an A_2 response) of an individual from category B_1 Similarly, p_{12}/p_{22} is the odds on an A_1 response of an individual from category B_2. Since the term on the left-hand side of equation (2.6) can be rewritten as $(p_{11}/p_{21}) \div (p_{12}/p_{22})$, this term is often referred to as the *odds ratio* (an alternative name is the *cross-product ratio*). The odds ratio is conventionally designated by the Greek symbol Ψ (psi) and will only be unity if A and B are independent.

Either of equations (2.5) or (2.6) could clearly provide the key to a test of independence. The actual probabilities will almost always be unknown, but we have a guide to their values—the observed proportions in the various cells—so that an estimate of p_{ij} is provided by

$$\hat{p}_{ij} = \frac{f_{ij}}{f_{00}} \qquad (2.7)$$

If A and B are independent, then from equation (2.5) we would expect that

$$\frac{f_{ij}}{f_{00}} \text{ would approximately equal } \frac{f_{i0}f_{0j}}{f_{00}^2}$$

Indeed, if A and B *are* independent, and we have a total of f_{00} observations in the table, then the most likely frequency in the (i, j) cell will be

$$e_{ij} = f_{00}\hat{p}_{ij} = \frac{f_{i0}f_{0j}}{f_{00}} \qquad (2.8)$$

So a comparison of this estimated frequency e_{ij}, which assumes independence, and the observed frequency f_{ij} will provide a basis for a test of the assumption of independence.

The usual tests for goodness of fit based on X^2 or Y^2 (see Chapter 1) are clearly applicable to this situation, since we are comparing observed and expected frequencies. The X^2 test takes the following simple form:

(a) Calculate $X^2 = \dfrac{f_{00}(f_{11}f_{22}-f_{12}f_{21})^2}{f_{10}f_{20}f_{01}f_{02}}$. (2.9)

(b) Compare the value of X^2 with tables of the χ_1^2 distribution.

Yates (1934) suggested an improvement to X^2 which he claimed would result in the test statistic being more closely approximated by the χ_1^2 distribution. His statistic X^{*2} is given by

$$X^{*2} = \frac{f_{00}(|f_{11}f_{22}-f_{12}f_{21}|-\tfrac{1}{2}f_{00})^2}{f_{10}f_{20}f_{01}f_{02}}$$ (2.10)

There has been considerable recent speculation concerning the relative merits of (2.9) and (2.10): Grizzle (1967) and Conover (1974) suggest that X^{*2} should be used if the frequency table was obtained by the equivalent of sampling method II given in Section 2.2 and that X^2 should be used for sampling method I. Baker (1977) provides an algorithm which calculates the exact probability distributions of X^2 (or X^{*2}) for small cell frequencies.

Example 2.1

Table 2.3. A hypothetical set of data

	B_1	B_2	Total
A_1	10	20	30
A_2	5	25	30
Total	15	45	60

For the data of Table 2.3 the value of X^2 is

$$X^2 = \frac{60(10 \times 25 - 5 \times 20)^2}{15 \times 45 \times 30 \times 30}$$

$$= 2.22$$

The value of X^{*2} is

$$X^{*2} = \frac{60(|10 \times 25 - 5 \times 20| - \tfrac{1}{2} \times 60)^2}{15 \times 45 \times 30 \times 30}$$

$$= 1.42$$

Reference to the tables of the χ_1^2 distribution shows that if A and B were independent then, even so, by chance, about 10 per cent. of the time we would expect to obtain a value of X^2 (or X^{*2}) greater than 2.71. Our values 2.22 and 1.42 are appreciably less than 2.71, which means that they are even more likely to have occurred by chance. We *cannot* reject the hypothesis that A and B are independent.

Notice that this does *not* mean that A and B *are* independent. Either they are independent or we had insufficient data to be able to detect their interdependence. As Mosteller (1968) points out, with a sufficiently large value of f_{00} it is possible to detect anything!

In our example both X^2 and X^{*2} were so small that we arrived at the same conclusion whichever one we used. There will be borderline cases where using X^2 we are inclined to reject the hypothesis of independence and using X^{*2} we are inclined to accept that hypothesis. The most sensible resolution of the dilemma would seem to be the production of the statement that it is unclear whether the hypothesis should be accepted or rejected! This is tantamount to evasion, but it should be appreciated that *any* conclusions one makes may be in error. For example, if X^2 had exactly a χ_1^2 distribution, then to accept the hypothesis of independence on obtaining an X^2 value of 2.709 would be wrong almost exactly 10 per cent of the time.

2.4. FISHER'S EXACT TEST

The χ^2 tests of independence described in the previous section relied on the test statistic having an approximate χ^2 distribution. This will certainly be the case when the expected cell frequencies are large, and is still a good approximation for quite small expected frequencies. However, when very small cell frequencies (say 5 or less) are involved the approximation ceases to be accurate and cannot be relied upon. Fortunately, for sampling scheme II, an alternative procedure suggested by Fisher is quite easy to use; this is described below.

If the two variables are denoted by A and B as before, then, if it is the A margins that are fixed by the sampling procedure, the hypothesis of independence is best expressed by (2.4), with (2.3) being appropriate for fixed B margins (the two formulations are, of course, equivalent). Now, given the values of the fixed marginal totals it is possible to calculate the probability of occurrence of any set of cell frequencies under the independence hypothesis. For Table 2.1 this probability is

$$P = \frac{f_{10}! \, f_{20}! \, f_{01}! \, f_{02}!}{f_{11}! \, f_{12}! \, f_{21}! \, f_{22}! \, f_{00}!} \tag{2.11}$$

where $m! = m \times (m-1) \times (m-2) \cdots 2 \times 1$ and $0! = 1$ ($m!$ is known as m factorial).

The basis of Fisher's test is to consider the more extreme configurations of the data that might have occurred and to compute the value of P for each of these. The exact probability of the observed configuration or a more extreme one occurring by chance is then the sum of these P values. If this sum turns out to be a very small probability, we conclude that it is unlikely that such a small value could have occurred by chance and we then reject the hypothesis of independence.

Example 2.2

We can use Fisher's exact test on the data of Table 2.3. We concentrate on the small (A_2, B_1) cell frequency and consider the probability of the observed subdivision or a more extreme subdivision of the thirty A_2 observations having occurred by chance under the hypothesis of independence between A and B. There are five more extreme configurations which might have been encountered, given the observed marginal totals of the table. These are set out in Table 2.4, together with their corresponding P values.

Table 2.4. Extreme configurations of the Table 2.3 data

11 19	12 18	13 17	14 16	15 15
4 26	3 27	2 28	1 29	0 30
$P = 0.0281$	$P = 0.0066$	$P = 0.0010$	$P = 0.0001$	$P = 0.0000$

The probability of the observed configuration given in Table 2.3 is found to be 0.0805 and therefore the overall probability of the observed configuration or a more extreme one is $0.0805 + 0.0281 + \cdots + 0.0000 = 0.1163$. We therefore accept the null hypothesis of independence between A and B.

Notice that Fisher's exact test is a one-sided test: the extreme configurations considered are those in which the proportion of B_2 to B_1 gets as large as possible for the A_2 category. At the other extreme, which is not of concern to us, the B_2 proportion would be as small as possible, which for the data of Table 2.3 would amount to a distribution of the thirty A_2 observations in the proportions 15 to 15. The χ^2 tests included in the previous section were two-tailed tests enquiring quite generally about independence. The appropriate χ^2 statistic for the fixed margin case is X^{*2} and the two tailed probability corresponding to the value of 1.42 which we obtained for the Table 2.3 data turns out to be 0.2330. To obtain the corresponding one-tailed probability, we divide the two-tailed probability by two, getting in this case 0.1165. Clearly the χ^2 approximation has been outstandingly successful for these data since 0.1165 is very close indeed to the exact 0.1163.

If the factorials are too large for pencil-and-paper calculation then, in the absence of a calculator with a factorial 'button', recourse should be made to tables of log factorials. Alternatively, and more simply, there are tables of critical configurations of the data for a wide range of (small) marginal totals. These tables appear in Finney *et al.* (1963) and are reproduced in the tables compiled by Pearson and Hartley (1966).

2.5. MEASURES OF ASSOCIATION

As we pointed out in Example 2.1, we can never be completely certain (without taking an infinitely large sample of respondents) whether or not the variables A and B are independent of one another. If they are not independent then it would be rather nice to have a measure of the extent to which they are related—a measure of association.

Over the years a large number of measures have been proposed. The reason for this variety is that they all measure slightly different aspects of association, and there is no clear-cut single aspect which predominates. Some measures are more suitable in some circumstances, but in other circumstances alternative measures may be preferable.

Although the advent of the log-linear model, which will be described in detail later, has to some extent outdated the use of *any* single measure of association, the continuing use of such measures in the literature and in computer packages requires us to spend some time studying them. One advantage that measures of association do possess is their relative simplicity of calculation.

2.6. YULE'S Q

Yule (1900) suggested the following coefficient of association:

$$Q = \frac{f_{11}f_{22} - f_{12}f_{21}}{f_{11}f_{22} + f_{12}f_{21}} \tag{2.12}$$

This measure has stood the test of time well; an excellent account of its use is provided by Davis (1971). Providing that the total frequency f_{00} is reasonably large, the distribution of Q is normal, with variance

$$\tfrac{1}{4}(1 - Q^2)^2 \left(\frac{1}{f_{11}} + \frac{1}{f_{12}} + \frac{1}{f_{21}} + \frac{1}{f_{22}} \right)$$

so that it is possible to obtain an approximate confidence interval for Q. The range of Q is $(-1, 1)$, the end points corresponding to complete (negative or positive) association, with 0 corresponding to no association (independence).

Example 2.3

For the data of Table 2.3 we have

$$Q = \frac{10 \times 25 - 5 \times 20}{10 \times 25 + 5 \times 20} = \frac{150}{350} = \frac{3}{7} = 0.43$$

and

$$\text{var}(Q) = \frac{1}{4}\left(\frac{40}{49}\right)^2\left(\frac{1}{10} + \frac{1}{5} + \frac{1}{20} + \frac{1}{25}\right) = 0.0650$$

The approximate 95 per cent. confidence interval for the true value of association, as measured by Q, is therefore

$$0.43 \pm 1.96\sqrt{0.0650}$$

that is

$$(-0.07, 0.93)$$

This confidence interval includes the value 0, the 'independence' value, so that the data do not rule out the possibility of independence (as measured by Q). This agrees with our previous X^2 test. Situations can occur, however, where Q appears significantly different from 0 even though the X^2 test does not dismiss the possibility of independence. This apparent confusion results from X^2 and Q measuring association in different ways. Statistical theory suggests that in cases of disagreement more attention should be paid to the X^2 test than the Q value.

2.7. THE ODDS RATIO

Intuitively one feels that if A and B are associated then the value of the measure of association should be unaltered by an increase in the number of observations; e.g. if every cell frequency were suddenly doubled we would not want our measure of association to be affected. Mosteller (1968) enlarged on this idea.

Simpson (1951) and Edwards (1963) have argued that the magnitude of a measure of association should not be affected by the order in which the categories of a variable are written down (though, of course, the sign of the measure might change).

These two distinct arguments both lead to the statistic

$$C = \frac{f_{11}f_{22}}{f_{12}f_{21}} \tag{2.13}$$

which is the sample odds ratio, analogous to Ψ defined by equation (2.6). Any function of C will also possess these same desirable properties. For example, we can rewrite the definition (2.12) of Q as

$$Q = \frac{C-1}{C+1}$$

so that it becomes clear that Q has these desirable properties.

The sample odds ratio itself seems to be a rather awkward function to work with, partly because of the problems that can arise with a zero observed cell frequency, and it is better to work with

$$\hat{\Psi} = \frac{(f_{11}+\frac{1}{2})(f_{22}+\frac{1}{2})}{(f_{12}+\frac{1}{2})(f_{21}+\frac{1}{2})} \qquad (2.14)$$

The range of $\hat{\Psi}$ is $(0, \infty)$, with 1 representing lack of association. This is distinctly unusual! A slightly more normal range of values is obtained by working with $\log_e(\hat{\Psi})$, which has the range $(-\infty, \infty)$, with 0 referring to the no-association situation.

The method for calculating an exact confidence interval for Ψ, using the estimate $\hat{\Psi}$, was found by Cornfield (1956) and Fisher (1962). Unfortunately, it is not straightforward and requires the use of one or other of the computer programs provided by Thomas (1971) and by Baptista and Pike (1977). Alternatively, there are a number of approximate confidence intervals that have been suggested, but Gart and Thomas (1972) found none to be very satisfactory.

At present, therefore, while the odds ratio $\hat{\Psi}$, or its natural logarithm, can be simply calculated, its use is limited by the lack of an easily obtained confidence interval. The use of the odds ratio at all may be unfamiliar to many. We have seen the theoretical reasons suggesting its use and when we come to study log-linear models later it will be seen that it is functions like C which play a central role.

2.8. GUTTMAN'S SYMMETRIC AND ASYMMETRIC λ VALUES

Goodman and Kruskal (1954) argue that for a measure of association to be of real value it should be capable of interpretation throughout its range (not just at -1, 0, and 1). They suggest a number of measures which have a probabilistic interpretation, of which the most well known are probably the measures λ_a, λ_b, and λ first suggested by Guttman (1941).

The basis of the Guttman measures is as follows. Suppose that an individual is chosen at random from the population and we are asked to guess his response to A, either (a) given no further information or (b) given his response to B. Clearly, the extra information provided in (b) can only *improve* our chance of being correct in our guess. If knowledge of the B response enables us to always be correct in our guess of the A response, then A and B must have a correlation of ± 1. If it never improves our chances then A and B must be uncorrelated. The Guttman λ measures are simple functions of the relative improvement in our chance of a correct guess.

At the risk of annoying the reader, we shall not present the formulae for the λ measures in this chapter but in the next chapter, which deals with the general $I \times J$ situation. This is partly to avoid tedious repetition, and partly because the λ measures do not work very well in the 2×2 situation—e.g. if the largest frequency in both rows lies in the same column, then λ_a will be 0 irrespective of the relative magnitudes of the frequencies involved.

2.9. GOODMAN AND KRUSKAL'S t MEASURES

In addition to the predictive λ measures, Goodman and Kruskal (1954) also suggest some very similar t measures, which will be discussed more fully in the next chapter. For the 2×2 case all three t measures (t_a, t_b, and t_{ab}) greatly simplify, each being equal to

$$\frac{(f_{11}f_{22} - f_{12}f_{21})^2}{f_{10}f_{20}f_{01}f_{02}} \tag{2.15}$$

which is simply the unmodified X^2 goodness-of-fit statistic (see equation 2.9) scaled by dividing by f_{00}.

2.10. MEASURES BASED DIRECTLY ON X^2

Because the basic test of independence is the χ^2 test, it would seem sensible to use the calculated value of X^2 as a measure of association. However, the range of X^2 is from 0 to ∞, which does not accord with the traditional range of -1 to 1. Various transformations have been suggested which include the following:

$$\phi = \left(\frac{X^2}{f_{00}}\right)^{1/2} \tag{2.16}$$

$$C = \left(\frac{X^2}{X^2 + f_{00}}\right)^{1/2}. \tag{2.17}$$

The statistic ϕ is sometimes referred to as the *root mean square contingency coefficient*; C is called the *coefficient of contingency*. A disadvantage of C is that its maximum value is $\sqrt{\frac{1}{2}}$ rather than 1. The square of ϕ, ϕ^2 is equal to the t values as given by (2.15), and is also equal to two further measures, Cramer's V and Tschuprow's T in their 2×2 forms.

All these measures suffer from the lack of any probabilistic interpretation and cannot be recommended.

2.11. CHOICE OF MEASURES OF ASSOCIATION

The purpose of a measure of association must be to provide a simple numerical answer to the question of the extent to which the two variables are related. If it is known that a certain measure of association takes the value 0.4 for the relation between A and B and the value 0.6 for the relation between C and D, then the presumption will be that there exists a stronger connection between C and D than there is between A and B. However, different measures of association focus their attention on different aspects of the relation between the variables, and it is quite possible that a second measure would provide values of 0.6 for the AB association and 0.4 for the CD association. Kruskal (1958) remarks that there is no reason to use a single measure of association; several measures of different types would give information of correspondingly different types—all that is required is an understanding of the way the measure works. We do not therefore pick a single 'best buy' of the measures discussed.

Hunter (1974) has examined how well various measures of association 'agreed' with each other and with one's intuitive views on the degrees of association present in different data sets. His conclusions, which have been criticized in an interesting series of replies by Hornung *et al.* (1975), were that the λ and t measures were preferable.

However, it is the belief of the author that, whichever measure is used, the user should obtain a corresponding confidence interval, so that he is aware of the uncertainty inherent in his point estimate. In Example 2.3 the statement '$Q = 0.43$' *is far more impressive* (*and thereby potentially misleading*) *than the statement that* 'Q *lies in the range* −0.07 *to* 0.93 *with* 95 *per cent. probability*'.

CHAPTER 3

Association and Independence in $I \times J$ Tables

3.1 CHI-SQUARED TESTS FOR INDEPENDENCE

We now consider the more general situation where A and B are polytomies rather than dichotomies. We suppose that there are I possible categories for variable A, which we label $A_1, A_2, \ldots, A_I$, and J possible categories for variable B ($B_1, B_2, \ldots, B_J$). Once again our natural first question is whether the two variables are independent. Our data consist of observed frequencies in a total of IJ cells, and we extend our previous notation in a natural fashion as shown in Table 3.1.

Table 3.1 Observed frequencies in an $I \times J$ table

	B_1	B_2	$\ldots$	B_J	Total
A_1	f_{11}	f_{12}	$\ldots$	f_{1J}	f_{10}
A_2	f_{21}	f_{22}	$\ldots$	f_{2J}	f_{20}
.	.	.		.	.
.	.	.		.	.
.	.	.		.	.
A_I	f_{I1}	f_{I2}	$\ldots$	f_{IJ}	f_{I0}
Total	f_{01}	f_{02}	$\ldots$	f_{0J}	f_{00}

The arguments used in the 2×2 situation carry over as one would expect: if A and B are independent then we would expect that the proportion of those in the jth column who were also in the ith row would be more or less the same for all the columns. Thus

$$\frac{f_{ij}}{f_{0j}} \simeq \frac{f_{i0}}{f_{00}} \qquad \text{for all } i \text{ and } j$$

Corresponding to the table of frequencies there is a table of theoretical probabilities, which follows precisely the same pattern. Writing p_{ij} for the probability that a randomly chosen individual from the sampled population is

23

a member of the (i, j) cell, the simple extension of the independence result (2.5) is that, if A and B are independent, then

$$p_{ij} = p_{i0}p_{0j} \qquad i = 1, 2, \ldots, I; j = 1, 2, \ldots, J \qquad (3.1)$$

Although the $\{p_{ij}\}$ are unknown, the ratios $\{f_{ij}/f_{00}\}$ provide estimates of them, and these estimates can be used to deduce the expected cell frequencies if A and B are independent, which are given by

$$e_{ij} = \frac{f_{i0}f_{0j}}{f_{00}} \qquad (3.2)$$

We introduced in Chapter 1 two tests of goodness of fit, the familiar X^2 statistic and the less familiar Y^2. Either of these can now be used to determine whether the $\{e_{ij}\}$ differ significantly from the $\{f_{ij}\}$ and thereby indicate a lack of independence between A and B. Whichever we use we need to know the appropriate number of degrees of freedom, which will be the same for both tests.

Consider the sum

$$e_{1j} + e_{2j} + \cdots + e_{Ij}$$

which from (3.2) can be rewritten as

$$\frac{(f_{10} + f_{20} + \cdots + f_{I0})f_{0j}}{f_{00}}. \qquad (3.3)$$

The bracketed term in (3.3) is simply f_{00} and so the sum of the expected frequencies in the column j turns out to be the sum of the observed frequencies in that column. A similar result is easily shown for the row totals. Since all these row and column totals are fixed in this way it follows that the individual $\{e_{ij}\}$ are subject to constraints. If we know $(I - 1)$ of the entries in a column, then, since the column total is known, we can deduce the remaining entry. A similar argument applies simultaneously to the rows and it turns out that if, for example, we know the values of the first $(I - 1)$ entries in the first $(J - 1)$ columns of expected values, then, since we know the marginal totals, we can deduce the remaining $(I + J - 1)$ entries. What all this means is that we have $(I - 1)(J - 1)$ degrees of freedom for our goodness-of-fit tests.

The form given for the X^2 test, viz.

$$X^2 = \sum_i \sum_j \frac{(f_{ij} - e_{ij})^2}{e_{ij}} \qquad (3.4)$$

is not usefully simplified by substituting for e_{ij}. However, the form for the Y^2 test,

$$Y^2 = 2 \sum_i \sum_j f_{ij} \log_e \left(\frac{f_{ij}}{e_{ij}} \right) \qquad (3.5)$$

can be made simpler by using the following piece of algebra:

$$\log_e\left(\frac{f_{ij}}{e_{ij}}\right) = \log_e\left(\frac{f_{ij}f_{00}}{f_{i0}f_{0j}}\right)$$

$$= \log_e(f_{ij}) + \log_e(f_{00}) - \log_e(f_{i0}) - \log_e(f_{0j}). \qquad (3.6)$$

Substitution of equation (3.6) in equation (3.5) gives the simpler form

$$Y^2 = 2\left\{\sum_i \sum_j f_{ij} \log_e(f_{ij}) - \sum_i f_{i0} \log_e(f_{i0}) - \sum_j f_{0j} \log_e(f_{0j}) + f_{00} \log_e(f_{00})\right\} \qquad (3.7)$$

The distributions of X^2 and Y^2 are only *approximately* χ^2. Yarnold (1970) shows that the approximation is good with expected cell frequencies down to about 3—he gives a formula for determining whether the approximation can be used in a particular case. Craddock and Flood (1970) provide tables of the distribution of X^2 for various small sample situations.

Example 3.1

Table 3.2   A fictitious set of frequencies

	B_1	B_2	B_3	B_4	Total
A_1	13	13	12	22	60
A_2	4	24	28	34	90
A_3	3	8	15	24	50
Total	20	45	55	80	200

Table 3.2 displays a (fictitious) set of data. Is there evidence that A and B are not independent? It is certainly very difficult to answer this by a simple visual scan of the data. We use equation (3.2) to obtain the expected frequencies under the hypothesis of independence. For example, e_{11}, the expected frequency of the top left-hand corner cell, is given by $60 \times 20 \div 200 = 6$. The complete set of expected frequencies is shown in Table 3.3.

Table 3.3   Expected frequencies under independence for the data of Table 3.2

	B_1	B_2	B_3	B_4	Total
A_1	6	13.5	16.5	24	60
A_2	9	20.25	24.75	36	90
A_3	5	11.25	13.75	20	50
Total	20	45	55	80	200

We now calculate the goodness-of-fit statistics. For example,

$$X^2 = \frac{(13-6)^2}{6} + \frac{(13-13.5)^2}{13.5} + \cdots + \frac{(24-20)^2}{20} = 16.25$$

$$Y^2 = 2\{[13 \log_e (13) + \cdots + 24 \log_e (24)] - [60 \log_e (60) + \cdots + 50 \log_e (50)]$$
$$- [20 \log_e (20) + \cdots + 80 \log_e (80)] + 200 \log_e (200)\}$$
$$= 2\{[33.34 + \cdots + 76.27] - [245.66 + \cdots + 195.60]$$
$$- [59.91 + \cdots + 350.56] + 1059.66\}$$
$$= 15.18$$

The upper 5 per cent point of a χ^2 distribution with $(4-1) \times (3-1) = 6$ degrees of freedom is 12.59. Both X^2 and Y^2 are substantially greater than 12.59, and we therefore conclude that the observed set of figures provides significant evidence that A and B are not independent.

3.2. LOCATING THE SOURCES OF LACK OF INDEPENDENCE

Whenever we have located some interdependence between the variables A and B we shall be interested in seeing how this interdependence manifests itself in the data. Occasionally, as we shall see in the example, it turns out that the entire interdependence is due to a single observation, and in such circumstances we would want to check the data in case an error (e.g. of transcription) had crept in. The simplest way of assessing the importance of the deviations between observed and expected frequencies is to look at the individual cell contributions to the X^2 statistic.

Example 3.2

For the data given in Table 3.2 we found that X^2 was 16.25. The individual cell contributions to X^2 are given in Table 3.4, from which it is clear that the major part of the 16.25 comes from the single cell (1,1).

Table 3.4   Contributions to X^2 for Table 3.2 data

	B_1	B_2	B_3	B_4
A_1	8.17	0.02	1.23	0.17
A_2	2.78	0.69	0.43	0.11
A_3	0.80	0.94	0.11	0.80

The immediate reaction to such a finding should be a check that the data are correct—perhaps the value 13 should have been 3.

3.3. PARTITIONING χ^2

We remarked in Chapter 1 that if X had a χ_a^2 distribution and Y had a χ_b^2 distribution, and if X and Y were independent, then $Z = X + Y$ has a χ_{a+b}^2 distribution. The corollary to this is that if W has a χ_c^2 distribution $(c > 1)$, then we can find c separate 1 degree-of-freedom components which together amount to W. For the situation that we encountered in our example we clearly would wish to subdivide the total of 6 degrees of freedom so that 1 degree of freedom related specifically to cell (1,1). The way to do it can only be learnt with practice. Maxwell (1961) gives a detailed treatment, and we give some relations below which may prove useful.

Rule 1   If there are c degrees of freedom for the original table then there can be no more than c subtables.

Rule 2   Each of the observed cell frequencies must appear in one and only one of the subtables.

Rule 3   Each subtable marginal total must either appear as a frequency in another subtable or must have been a marginal total of the original table.

Example 3.3

The table of frequencies, Table 3.2, was seen to be in reasonable accord with the table of expected values under the hypothesis of independence, with the exception of the very large frequency in cell (1,1). To isolate this frequency we form Table 3.5, which dichotomizes the variables A and B leaving the (1,1) entry as one of the entries in the new table. The values of the goodness-of-fit statistics for these data are calculated in the usual way, and have $(2-1) \times (2-1) = 1$ degrees of freedom. We find that $X^2 = 12.96$ and $Y^2 = 11.73$.

Table 3.5 Double dichotomy of Table 3.2 data, isolating cell (1,1)

	B_1	Not B_1	Total
A_1	13	47	60
Not A_1	7	133	140
Total	20	180	200

There remain a further 5 degrees of freedom to be allocated. There are many ways of doing this. One, that seemed sensible to the author, is illustrated in the three parts of Table 3.6.

The reader is invited to check that this subdivision satisfies the rules given earlier, and may also notice certain other symmetries (e.g. the row and column captions).

Table 3.6   Subdivision of the remaining 5 degrees of freedom

(a)

	B_2	B_3	B_4	Total
A_2	24	28	34	86
A_3	8	15	24	47
Total	32	43	58	133

(b)

	B_2	B_3	B_4	Total
A_1	13	12	22	47
Not A_1	32	43	58	133
Total	45	55	80	180

(c)

	B_1	Not B_1	Total
A_2	4	86	90
A_3	3	47	50
Total	7	133	140

The values of X^2 and Y^2 for these three tables should also be calculated, and a summary of the results is given in Table 3.7. It is worth recalling that for the full 3×4 table we had 16.25 for X^2 and 15.18 for Y^2, each with 6 degrees of freedom. The slight difference between the total here of 16.26 and the previous 16.25 is solely due to round-off errors.

Table 3.7   Results of partitioning Table 3.2

Table	Degrees of freedom	X^2	Y^2
3.5	1	12.96	11.73
3.6(a)	2	2.36	2.49
3.6(b)	2	0.78	0.80
3.6(c)	1	0.16	0.16
Total	6	16.26	15.18

We can now provide a more comprehensive interpretation of the relation between variables A and B. Since none of the subtables of Table 3.6 shows any significant departure from that which would be expected if A and B were independent, we can state that the variables A and B behave as if they were independent, with the exception that if an individual belongs to category A_1 then he is much more likely than would otherwise have been expected to belong to category B_1 (and vice versa). The physical interpretation of this would require knowledge of the nature of the variables and their categories.

3.4. MEASURES OF ASSOCIATION FOR $I \times J$ TABLES

As an alternative to testing for independence between the two variables or to provide a simple and quick quantification of the extent of independence between the variables, data analysts often provide the value of some measure of association. However, as was remarked in the previous chapter, many of the oft-quoted measures of association have no direct probabilistic interpretation—in other words, they are just numbers.

There are two major classes of variable with which we shall be concerned. A *nominal* variable has names for its categories; these names have no natural order. For example, the variable 'fruit' might have the categories 'apple', 'orange', and 'banana' which could reasonably be presented in any of the six possible orders. The second class of variable is termed *ordinal* and refers to a variable with ordered categories. An example is the variable 'age', with categories <20, 21–30, 31–40, >40; it would be most unreasonable to present these categories in, for example, the order 21–30, >40, <20, 31–40.

In the sections that follow we analyse several of the most frequently used of the measures of association, starting with those more appropriate for nominal data and then treating those appropriate for ordinal data.

3.5. MEASURING ASSOCIATION USING λ_b

The three λ measures, λ_b, λ_a, and λ, are very similar in character. We describe λ_b in detail in this section and λ_a and λ more briefly in the following section.

The statistic λ_b involves a comparison of the following two situations: an individual is chosen at random from the population and we are asked to guess to which B category the individual belongs, either (a) given no further information or (b) given his A category. If the responses A and B are totally unrelated then we can do no better in the second situation than we did in the first, but otherwise there will be an improvement. The measure λ_b quantifies this improvement as the relative decrease in the probability of error in guessing the B category as between the two situations under the assumption that our guess consists of selecting the most likely of the B categories on each occasion:

$$\lambda_b = \frac{\sum_{i=1}^{I} f_{im} - f_{0m}}{f_{00} - f_{0m}}. \tag{3.8}$$

where f_{im} is the largest entry in the ith row of the table and f_{0m} is the largest of the column marginal totals. For a more detailed discussion see Goodman and Kruskal (1954).

Example 3.4

Table 3.8   A second set of hypothetical cell frequencies

	B_1	B_2	B_3	B_4	Total
A_1	10	5	18	20	53
A_2	8	16	5	13	42
A_3	11	7	3	4	25
Total	29	28	26	37	120

For the data given in Table 3.8 the largest observations in the three rows are $f_{1m} = 20$, $f_{2m} = 16$, and $f_{3m} = 11$, while the largest column total is $f_{0m} = 37$. So

$$\lambda_b = \frac{(20+16+11)-37}{120-37} = \frac{10}{83} = 0.12.$$

Example 3.5

The data of Table 3.2 illustrate the problem that the λ measures encounter with uneven marginal totals. The problem becomes apparent when we locate the row maxima, which are $f_{1m} = 22$, $f_{2m} = 34$, and $f_{3m} = 24$; all three are in the third column, which has therefore the greatest marginal total ($f_{0m} = 80$). The consequence is that

$$\lambda_b = \frac{(22+34+24)-80}{200-80} = 0$$

3.6. MEASURING ASSOCIATION USING λ_a OR λ

If the roles of A and B are interchanged so that we are interested in our increased effectiveness of predicting the A category when the B category is known, then the corresponding statistic is

$$\lambda_a = \frac{\sum_{j=1}^{J} f_{mj} - f_{m0}}{f_{00} - f_{m0}} \tag{3.9}$$

where f_{mj} is the largest entry in the jth column of the table and f_{m0} is the largest of the row marginal totals.

In many cases it would be unreasonable to focus attention on either of the two variables at the expense of the other. If we assume that A is of interest for half the time and B for the other half, then this leads to the measure

$$\lambda = \frac{(\Sigma_{i=1}^{I} f_{im} - f_{0m}) + (\Sigma_{j=1}^{J} f_{mj} - f_{m0})}{2f_{00} - f_{m0} - f_{0m}} \qquad (3.10)$$

Example 3.6

For the data displayed in Table 3.8 we have

$$f_{m1} = 11 \qquad f_{m2} = 16 \qquad f_{m3} = 18 \qquad f_{m4} = 20 \quad \text{and} \quad f_{m0} = 53$$

consequently,

$$\lambda_a = \frac{(11+16+18+20) - 53}{120 - 53} = \frac{12}{67} = 0.18$$

Using these results and those of Example 3.4 we get

$$\lambda = \frac{12+10}{67+83} = \frac{22}{150} = 0.15.$$

Note that λ must take a value between λ_a and λ_b.

Example 3.7

For the more awkward data of Table 3.2 we have

$$f_{m1} = 13 \qquad f_{m2} = 24 \qquad f_{m3} = 28 \qquad f_{m4} = 34 \quad \text{and} \quad f_{m0} = 90$$

so that

$$\lambda_a = \frac{99 - 90}{200 - 90} = \frac{9}{110} = 0.08$$

Also, using the results of Example 3.5,

$$\lambda = \frac{9+0}{110+120} = \frac{9}{230} = 0.04$$

3.7. CONFIDENCE INTERVALS FOR THE λ MEASURES

These λ measures give an impression of the association that exists between the variables. However, it can be very misleading, as we mentioned in connection with Q in the previous chapter, to make the bold statement that '$\lambda_b = 0.12$'. The value that we obtain is an estimate of an unknown population value, and it is for this value, which we shall call L_b, that we obtain an estimated confidence interval.

Goodman and Kruskal (1963) have obtained approximations to the distributions of each of the λ values. For λ_b they show that the following quantity:

$$(L_b - \lambda_b)\sqrt{\frac{(f_{00} - f_{0m})^3}{(f_{00} - \Sigma_i f_{im})(\Sigma_i f_{im} + f_{0m} - 2\Sigma_i f_{im})}} \tag{3.11}$$

has an approximate unit normal distribution. Here $\Sigma_i f_{im}$ denotes the sum of the f_{im} over those values of i such that f_{im} occurs in the column which has the largest column total. Fortunately, this is not as difficult as it appears.

A corresponding quantity to (3.11), with row and column totals interchanged, provides the confidence interval for λ_a, though the formula for λ is more complicated.

Example 3.8

We consider once again the data of Table 3.8. The column with the largest total is column 4 (total 37), and this column includes the figure 20, which was the largest entry in row 1. However, this column does not include the other row maxima (16 and 11) so that $\Sigma_i f_{im} = 20$.

Substituting in (3.11) we obtain

$$(L_b - 0.12)\sqrt{\frac{(120 - 37)^3}{(120 - 47)(47 + 37 - 2 \times 20)}}$$

$$= (L_b - 0.12)\sqrt{\frac{83^3}{73 \times 44}}$$

$$= (L_b - 0.12) \times 13.34.$$

Since 13.34 $(L_b - 0.12)$ has a unit normal distribution we can write immediately that an approximate symmetric confidence interval for L_b is

$$0.12 \pm \frac{1.96}{13.34}$$

or

$$(-0.03, 0.27)$$

Notice that this confidence interval includes negative values, which are impossible since $L_b \geq 0$; an approximation is clearly involved.

The corresponding confidence interval for L_a turns out to be $(0.01, 0.35)$.

3.8 MEASURES OF ASSOCIATION BASED ON X^2.

In Section 2.10 we mentioned various functions of X^2. Both the two whose formulae were given in that section, ϕ and C, can be used equally for $I \times J$

tables as for 2×2 tables, with the definition being those given in equations (2.16) and (2.17).

Two further measures are Cramer's V and Tschuprow's T which are defined by

$$V = \left\{ \frac{X^2}{f_{00} \times \min\left[(I-1), (J-1)\right]} \right\}^{1/2} \tag{3.12}$$

$$T = \left[\frac{X^2/f_{00}}{\sqrt{(I-1)(J-1)}} \right]^{1/2} \tag{3.13}$$

Confusingly, both ϕ and V are occasionally given in squared form. This serves to underline the proliferation and lack of coherence of these measures which are all attempts to find a function of X^2 limited to the range $(0, 1)$.

Example 3.9

In Example 3.1 we found that the value of X^2 for the data of Table 3.2 was 15.18. Consequently,

$$V = \left(\frac{16.25}{2 \times 200} \right)^{1/2} = 0.202$$

$$T = \left(\frac{16.25}{200\sqrt{6}} \right)^{1/2} = 0.182$$

$$\phi = \left(\frac{16.25}{200} \right)^{1/2} = 0.285$$

$$C = \left(\frac{16.25}{216.25} \right)^{1/2} = 0.274$$

It is obvious that V and T will always be rather similar, with $V = T$ for square tables and $V > T$ otherwise. Similarly, ϕ and C will be very similar with ϕ always greater than C.

3.9. GOODMAN AND KRUSKAL'S t MEASURES

We have seen that problems can exist when using the Guttman λ measures (Example 3.5), and in an attempt to circumvent these Goodman and Kruskal (1954) suggested their t measures which are very similar in character. The difference lies in a change in the method of predicting the category of one variable given the category of the other variable. Instead of always predicting the most probable category, with the t measures the various categories are all predicted in proportion to their observed category totals.

The resulting measures look rather more like X^2 than the λ measures. For example,

$$t_b = \frac{\Sigma\Sigma_{ij} \left[(f_{00}f_{ij} - f_{i0}f_{0j})^2 / f_{i0}\right]}{f_{00}(f_{00}^2 - \Sigma_j f_{0j}^2)} \tag{3.14}$$

with equivalent formulae for t_a and t. Goodman and Kruskal (1972) provide the sampling variances for these measures. Alternative approaches to improving the λ measures have been suggested by Acock (1974) and Mosteller (1968).

Example 3.10

For the data of Table 3.2 we obtain

$$t_b = \frac{1}{200(200^2 - 20^2 - 45^2 - 55^2 - 80^2)}$$

$$\times \left[\frac{(200 \times 13 - 20 \times 60)^2}{60} + \cdots + \frac{(200 \times 24 - 50 \times 80)^2}{50} \right]$$

$$= 0.02$$

3.10. MEASURES OF ASSOCIATION FOR ORDINAL TABLES

In the next three sections we describe three measures of association which are all based on the same essential characteristics of the table. The basis of these measures is that the I ordered categories of variable A represent I possible ranks for the total of f_{00} observations. We shall refer to those observations which are assigned to category 1 of variable A as being ranked higher than those in category 2, and so on, with a corresponding ranking for variable B. With positive association between A and B we can expect an observation that is highly ranked for variable A to be highly ranked for variable B, and one that is lowly ranked for variable A to be lowly ranked for variable B.

Consider a typical pair of observations, one belonging to cell (i, j)—that is to category i of variable A and category j of variable B—and the other to cell (i', j'). The ordinal measures of association are all simple functions of the following four quantities:

S = total number of pairs of observations for which *either* both $i > i'$ and $j > j'$ *or* both $i < i'$ and $j < j'$
D = total number of pairs of observations for which *either* both $i > i'$ and $j < j'$ *or* both $i < i'$ and $j > j'$
T_a = total number of pairs of observations for which $i = i'$
T_b = total number of pairs of observations for which $j = j'$

When there is strong association between the variables A and B the number S will be large and the number D will be small, and it is natural therefore to concentrate on the size of the difference, $S-D$. All three measures that we describe are different standardized versions of $S-D$.

3.11. GOODMAN AND KRUSKAL'S γ

Goodman and Kruskal (1954) proposed the following measure:

$$\gamma = \frac{S-D}{S+D} \tag{3.15}$$

This measure has a direct probalistic interpretation, namely as the difference between the probabilities of like and unlike orders for two observations chosen at random from the population, conditional on their not having tied ranks.

If the variables A and B are independent of one another then on average γ will take the value 0. However, if $\gamma = 0$ this does not necessarily imply that A and B are independent; it is possible, as Goodman and Kruskal illustrate, to construct tables in which $\gamma = 0$ and yet A and B are clearly not independent. The range of values for γ is -1 to 1.

The sampling distribution of γ is approximately normal, and its variance, which is tedious to calculate without a computer, is given by Goodman and Kruskal (1963) and in an alternative form by Goodman and Kruskal (1972).

Example 3.11

We illustrate the method for calculating S and D using the data of Table 3.2, which is reproduced here as Table 3.9 to facilitate understanding of the necessary calculations.

Table 3.9   The data of Table 3.2 illustrating the method for calculating S and D

	B_1	B_2	B_3	B_4
A_1	13	13	12	22
A_2	4	24	28	34
A_3	3	8	15	24

To calculate S we consider each cell in turn, multiplying the frequency in that cell by the total frequency in the block of cells directly below and to the right. Thus, as shown in Table 3.9, the frequency of 13 in cell $(1, 1)$ is multiplied by the total frequency in the 2×3 rectangle at the bottom right (this is $24 + 28 + 34 + 8 + 15 + 24 = 133$). The aggregate of these $(I-1)(J-1)$ cross-products is S. Thus for Table 3.9 we have

$$S = 13(24 + 28 + 34 + 8 + 15 + 24) + 13(28 + 34 + 15 + 24) + 12(34 + 24)$$
$$+ 4(8 + 15 + 24) + 24(15 + 24) + 28(24)$$
$$= 5534$$

The quantity D is calculated in a very similar manner, though for D each cell is multiplied by the total frequency in the block of cells directly below and to the left. Thus we have

$$D = 22(4 + 24 + 28 + 3 + 8 + 15) + 12(4 + 24 + 3 + 8) + 13(4 + 3) + 34(3 + 8 + 15)$$
$$+ 28(3 + 8) + 24(3)$$
$$= 3627$$

Finally, using equation (3.15) we have

$$\gamma = \frac{5534 - 3627}{5534 + 3627} = 0.208$$

An alternative method for calculating S and D is presented by Leathers (1977), who provides the necessary computer algorithm.

3.12. KENDALL'S t

Kendall's t is a familiar measure of rank correlation which in its original form assumed that the two rankings to be compared contained no tied ranks. In the present context there are, of course, large numbers of ties and one of the suggested adaptations, which we shall denote by t_K to distinguish it from the Goodman–Kruskal t measures described in Section 3.9, is given by

$$t_K = \frac{2(S-D)}{\sqrt{(S+D+T_a)(S+D+T_b)}} \tag{3.16}$$

where T_a and T_b were defined in Section 3.10.

Example 3.12

In Example 3.11 we calculated the values of S and D for the data given in Tables 3.2 and 3.9. The value of T_a is obtained by multiplying each cell frequency by the sum of the cell frequencies to its right in the same row. The aggregate of the $I(J-1)$ cross-products of this type is T_a. Thus, for our data,

$$T_a = 13(13 + 12 + 22) + 13(12 + 22) + 12(22) + 4(24 + 28 + 34) + \cdots + 15(24)$$
$$= 4914$$

The quantity T_b is calculated column-wise in the corresponding fashion, giving for our data,

$$T_b = 13(4+3)+4(3)+\cdots+34(24)=3739$$

Using these frequencies we have

$$t_K = \frac{2\times 1907}{\sqrt{14075\times 12900}} = 0.283$$

A useful check on the accuracy of the computations is provided by the relation

$$f_{00}^2 = 2(S+D+T_a+T_b)+\sum_i\sum_j f_{ij}^2 \qquad (3.17)$$

In our example $f_{00}^2 = 40,000$ and $\Sigma\Sigma_{ij}f_{ij}^2 = 4372$, and using (3.17) we conclude that our calculations have been accurate.

3.13. SOMERS' d

Somers (1962) suggested a variation of the preceding statistics which is claimed to be more appropriate when one of the variables, B, can be regarded as dependent on the other variable, A. This statistic, which we denote by d_{ba}, is defined by

$$d_{ba} = \frac{S-D}{S+D+T_b} \qquad (3.18)$$

This statistic can be interpreted as the difference between the probabilities of like and unlike orders for two observations chosen at random from the population, conditional on their not having tied ranks for variable A. The statistic is approximately normally distributed with the variance given by Goodman and Kruskal (1972).

Example 3.13

Continuing with the analysis of Table 3.9, we find

$$d_{ba} = \frac{1907}{12900} = 0.148$$

while the corresponding alternative statistic, regarding A as the dependent variable, is

$$d_{ab} = \frac{1907}{14075} = 0.135$$

3.14. COMPARISON OF THE MEASURES OF ASSOCIATION

As we remarked in discussing the measures of association for 2×2 tables, each of the measures is relevant to a different aspect of the association between the variables. We should not be worried by differences in the magnitudes of the various measures. For example, during the course of this chapter we have found the following values for measures of association for the data in Table 3.2: $\lambda_b = 0$, $t_b = 0.02$, $\lambda = 0.04$, $\lambda_a = 0.08$, $d_{ab} = 0.135$, $d_{ba} = 0.148$, $T = 0.182$, $V = 0.202$, $\gamma = 0.208$, $C = 0.274$, $t_K = 0.283$, and $\phi = 0.285$.

All these measures, with the exception of Goodman and Kruskal's t_b, may be calculated automatically using the statistics subroutine provided by Nie *et al.* (1975).

A personal choice of these measures would be Goodman and Kruskal's λ (for nominal data) or γ (for ordinal data), if the two variables are of equal importance, and Goodman and Kruskal's λ_b or Somers' d_{ba} if variable B depends on variable A.

None of these measures should, however, be regarded as much more than a simple preliminary calculation before a more detailed analysis.

CHAPTER 4

Association and Independence in Multidimensional Tables

4.1. INTRODUCTION

In this chapter we commence our study of the problems that arise when a cross-classification involves more than two variables. We begin by extending the notation to the general situation and continue by examining the various ways in which independence can be manifested in multidimensional tables. Some of the apparently paradoxical situations that can arise are also discussed.

For simplicity, most of the discussion will be couched in terms of a three-way table, with variables A, B, and C having I, J, and K categories respectively. In the examples I, J, and K are equal to 2.

4.2. THE NOTATION FOR A THREE-WAY TABLE

Our data consist of the observed frequencies in a total of $I \times J \times K$ cells. We write f_{ijk} for the observed frequency in cell (i, j, k), which is situated in row i, column j, and layer k of the three-way table. We denote the corresponding probability of an individual observation, chosen at random from the population, belonging to this cell as p_{ijk}.

There are now two different classes of marginal total. The one-variable marginal totals, which represent the totals of individual rows, columns, or layers, are typified by

$$f_{0jk} = \sum_i f_{ijk} \qquad (4.1)$$

with the corresponding marginal probability being p_{0jk}. The second class of marginal total represents the total of an entire wedge of the three-way table and is typified by

$$f_{00k} = \sum_j f_{0jk} = \sum_i f_{i0k} = \sum_i \sum_j f_{ijk} \qquad (4.2)$$

with p_{00k} as the corresponding probability.

39

Example 4.1.

Table 4.1. A fictitious set of data displaying mutual independence of A, B, and C

	C_1				C_2		
	B_1	B_2	Total		B_1	B_2	Total
A_1	6	18	24	A_1	9	27	36
A_2	4	12	16	A_2	6	18	24
Total	10	30	40	Total	15	45	60

Consider the fictitious data given in Table 4.1. There are four one-variable marginal totals corresponding to variable B: these are $f_{101} = 24$, $f_{201} = 16$, $f_{102} = 36$, and $f_{202} = 24$. There are two two-variable marginal totals corresponding to variable C, which are $f_{001} = 40$ and $f_{002} = 60$. The corresponding two-variable marginal totals for A are more easily seen by presenting the same set of numbers in a different way as in Table 4.2, where it is clear that $f_{100} = 60$ and $f_{200} = 40$.

Table 4.2. An alternative presentation of Table 4.1

	A_1				A_2		
	B_1	B_2	Total		B_1	B_2	Total
C_1	6	18	24	C_1	4	12	16
C_2	9	27	36	C_2	6	18	24
Total	15	45	60	Total	10	30	40

4.3. MUTUAL INDEPENDENCE OF A, B, AND C

The definition of independence for the cross-classification of two variables was given by the relation (3.1), and this extends naturally to the three-variable situation as follows:

$$p_{ijk} = p_{i00}p_{0j0}p_{00k} \qquad i = 1, \ldots, I; \; j = 1, \ldots, J; \; k = 1, \ldots, K \qquad (4.3)$$

If the relation (4.3) does hold for all the cell probabilities then the variables A, B, and C are said to be mutually independent.

Example 4.2.

The data given in Table 4.1 (and, of course, Table 4.2) is in exact accord with the relation (4.3). For example, $f_{100} = 60$, $f_{020} = 75$, and $f_{002} = 60$. The maximum likelihood estimates of the corresponding probabilities are $\hat{p}_{100} =$

$f_{100}/f_{000} = 0.60$, and similarly $\hat{p}_{020} = 0.75$ and $\hat{p}_{002} = 0.60$. From the relation (4.3) we therefore obtain $\hat{p}_{122} = 0.60 \times 0.75 \times 0.60 = 0.27$, which is equal to $f_{122}/f_{000} = 27/100$.

4.4. CONDITIONAL INDEPENDENCE

If we consider a two-variable wedge taken from the three-variable table, then this is just like one of the two-way tables that we looked at in previous chapters. Applying the two-variable independence definition (3.1) to such a wedge, we arrive at a relation typified by

$$p_{ijk} = \frac{p_{i0k}p_{0jk}}{p_{00k}} \qquad (4.4)$$

When the variables satisfy the relation (4.4) we say that the variables A and B are conditionally independent of one another given the category of C.

If A, B, and C display mutual independence then, of course, the relation (4.4) and the equivalent relation for the other pairs of variables will automatically hold.

Example 4.3

Table 4.3. Data displaying conditional independence

	C_1				C_2		
	B_1	B_2	Total		B_1	B_2	Total
A_1	15	5	20	A_1	28	12	40
A_2	15	5	20	A_2	42	18	60
Total	30	10	40	Total	70	30	100

Table 4.3 illustrates a set of data in which A and B are clearly independent at either of the two categories of C. In the table the left-hand subtable refers to category C_1 and the right-hand subtable to category C_2. The left-hand subtable's independence is manifest; the right-hand table's independence is confirmed by noting that $40 \times 70/100 = 28$.

An alternative way of confirming the independence is to calculate the odds ratio. For the C_1 table $\Psi = (15 \times 5) \div (15 \times 5) = 1.0$ and for the C_2 table $\Psi = (28 \times 18) \div (42 \times 12) = 1.0$. The value 1.0 corresponds, of course, to the independence situation.

Table 4.4. Rearrangement of the data of Table 4.3

	B_1				B_2		
	C_1	C_2	Total		C_1	C_2	Total
A_1	15	28	43	A_1	5	12	17
A_2	15	42	57	A_2	5	18	23
Total	30	70	100	Total	10	30	40

As an illustration of the fact that A and B can be independent without either A or B being independent of C consider Table 4.4, which is simply an alternative presentation of the data of Table 4.3. Both subtables display the same type of pattern, but it is not a pattern of independence; the odds ratio for both tables is 1.5 and not 1.0. Similarly, the subtables for B against C subdivided by the levels of A both display odds ratios of 9/7.

Table 4.5. Collapse of Table 4.3 over the C response

	B_1	B_2	Total
A_1	43	17	60
A_2	57	23	80
Total	100	40	140

One of the 'paradoxes' referred to earlier is manifest by Table 4.5, which shows what happens if C is ignored and the two subtables of Table 4.3 are amalgamated. Despite A and B being independent at either level of C, they do not appear independent in Table 4.5.

This illustrates a most important point: the common practice of researchers of collapsing their multidimensional data into a series of two-way tables could well result in their reaching misleading conclusions.

4.5. MULTIPLE INDEPENDENCE OF C WITH A AND B

If two of the variables, A and B, say, display the same pattern of association for every category of the third variable, C, then clearly the pattern of association between A and B is unaffected by C and we say that C is independent of (AB). Algebraically this is represented by

$$p_{ijk} = p_{ij0}p_{00k} \qquad (4.5)$$

Example 4.4

The data given in Table 4.6 shows a set of data displaying perfect agreement with equation (4.5).

Table 4.6. Data displaying multiple independence

	C_1				C_2		
	B_1	B_2	Total		B_1	B_2	Total
A_1	6	10	16	A_1	9	15	24
A_2	4	20	24	A_2	6	30	36
Total	10	30	40	Total	15	45	60

These data display a strong association between variables A and B for each category of C. Since the association is identical in form for both tables—the numbers in the right-hand subtable being 1.5 times the corresponding numbers in the left-hand subtable—we can state that C is independent of (AB). The odds ratio for each of the subtables is 3.0.

4.6. SIMPSON'S PARADOX

We saw in Section 4.4 one of the 'funny' things that can happen when a multidimensional table is collapsed over the categories of a variable. The most striking of the possibilities of this type was first pointed out by Simpson (1951). Subsequent discussion has been provided by Birch (1963) and Blyth (1972). Table 4.7 illustrates the situation.

Table 4.7. Illustration of Simpson's paradox

	C_1				C_2		
	B_1	B_2	Total		B_1	B_2	Total
A_1	95	800	895	A_1	400	5	405
A_2	5	100	105	A_2	400	195	595
Total	100	900	1000	Total	800	200	1000

In the left-hand subtable of Table 4.7 the variables A and B display positive association; the odds ratio is $(95 \times 100)/(800 \times 5) = 19/8$, which is considerably greater than 1, the independence value. In the right-hand subtable the association is even more strongly positive with an odds ratio of 19.0.

On pooling the two tables, collapsing the three-way table over the categories of C, we obtain Table 4.8.

Table 4.8. Collapsed version of Table 4.7.

	B_1	B_2	Total
A_1	495	805	1300
A_2	405	295	700
Total	900	1100	2000

The association between A and B which is displayed in Table 4.8 is *negative* (odds ratio $= (495 \times 295)/(805 \times 405) = 0.45$, appreciably *less* than 1), whereas the two constituent tables both showed a *positive* association!

4.7. THE INTERPRETATION AND DEFINITION OF THREE-FACTOR INTERACTIONS

The data presented in the previous examples were, of course, fictitious. In real life we can expect random variation to cloud the picture. However, it is not difficult to imagine that these kinds of equality of relation could hold for the underlying cell probabilities. It is instructive to see what equality of odds ratios in the subtables would imply. We would have for the $2 \times 2 \times 2$ table

$$\frac{p_{111}p_{221}}{p_{121}p_{211}} = \frac{p_{112}p_{222}}{p_{122}p_{212}} \tag{4.6}$$

When equality holds in (4.6) we clearly have a very special situation, and in the more usual situation we could expect inequality of these odds ratios. In other words, the ratio of the two odds ratios might be usually expected to be non-unity, with unity referring to the special situation that we encountered in Example 4.4.

We see that we have the beginnings of a hierarchical system: first odds, then odds ratios, and now ratios of odds ratios! Recognition of this pattern led Bartlett (1935) to suggest that the ratio of the two sides of (4.6) was the basis of the definition of a *second-order* or *three-factor interaction*.

Roy and Kastenbaum (1956) generalized Bartlett's suggestion to the general $I \times J \times K$ situation as follows. There is no three-factor interaction between the variables A, B, and C if and only if

$$\frac{p_{IJK}p_{ijK}}{p_{iJK}p_{IjK}} = \frac{p_{IJk}p_{ijk}}{p_{iJk}p_{Ijk}} \tag{4.7}$$

for $i = 1, 2, \ldots, (I-1)$, $j = 1, 2, \ldots, (J-1)$, and $k = 1, 2, \ldots, (K-1)$.

4.8. ANALYSING ASSOCIATION IN MULTIWAY TABLES

The problems of the researcher faced with a three-dimensional array of cell frequencies can easily be seen to be formidable. As we have shown, the 'obvious' techniques, such as studying the data two variables at a time, can lead to an obscuring of the structure of the data and possibly to incorrect conclusions.

Not only do we have to worry about the 'simple' association that exists between two variables, but we also have to face the possibility of more complex multiway associations. Example 4.3 illustrated a situation in which the AC and BC associations existed, but for which there was no AB interaction nor the three-factor ABC association. In Example 4.4 the only interaction was that between A and B.

Goodman (1969) discussed methods of partitioning the X^2 goodness-of-fit statistic (which can be used in the usual way with the estimated frequencies being calculated from the relation (4.3)). However, Goodman's subsequent work (1970, 1971a) on developing the log-linear model into a practicable analytical tool would seem to have largely supplanted the earlier techniques. We study these new techniques in the following chapters.

For an extended discussion of the various possible manifestations of independence in four-way and more complex tables, see Kastenbaum (1974).

Log-linear Models for 2×2 Tables

5.1. INTRODUCTION

The last three chapters have been concerned with detecting and measuring the association between variables. This has been done in a somewhat haphazard fashion, and the measures of association in particular have had little theoretical backing. In contrast, we develop in this and the two succeeding chapters a coherent and structured procedure, which allows the analyst to confidently identify simple and complex associations between two or more variables in a multivariable situation. In the last five or six years the development of the analysis of this type of data has received a great deal of attention from many authors: scarcely an issue of any of the major statistical journals has passed without some further article advancing the theory. The principal author of this work has been Professor Leo Goodman, and it is on the papers by Goodman (1970, 1971a, 1971b, 1972a, 1972b) that this account is principally based. An excellent layman's account is provided by Davis (1974).

5.2. THE OBJECT OF USING A MODEL

A simple demonstration of the need for a model is provided by considering an artificial data set in which all the variables are mutually independent and from which all random variation has been removed. One such data set is shown in Table 5.1.

One perfectly valid explanation of this data would be to suppose that it consisted of 600 observations, randomly selected from a population in which the cell probabilities were as follows:

$$p_{111} = \frac{12}{600} \qquad p_{112} = \frac{24}{600} \qquad p_{121} = \frac{3}{600} \qquad \cdots \qquad p_{442} = \frac{44}{600}$$

Since we know that the probabilities sum to 1, there would be $(4 \times 4 \times 2) - 1 = 31$ independent parameters in this list.

Such an explanation, although valid, could not be described as being particularly enlightening! Much more enlightening is the following simpler model, which requires only seven parameters. This model notices that the probability of being in cell (i, j, k), p_{ijk}, can be determined from the appropriate marginal probabilities by calculating

$$p_{ijk} = p_{i00}p_{0j0}p_{00k} \tag{5.1}$$

Consequently, knowing that the probabilities sum to 1, it is sufficient to know (5.1) and the values of p_{100}, p_{200}, p_{300}, p_{010}, p_{020}, p_{030}, and p_{001} to obtain the value of any individual cell probability. By being able to use the model (5.1) we have been able to specify the data with seven rather than thirty-one parameters—a spectacular, and by no means atypical, saving.

Table 5.1. Hypothetical data on three mutually independent variables

	C_1				
	B_1	B_2	B_3	B_4	Total
A_1	12	3	9	6	30
A_2	8	2	6	4	20
A_3	16	4	12	8	40
A_4	44	11	33	22	110
Total	80	20	60	40	200

	C_2				
	B_1	B_2	B_3	B_4	Total
A_1	24	6	18	12	60
A_2	16	4	12	8	40
A_3	32	8	24	16	80
A_4	88	22	66	44	220
Total	160	40	120	80	400

Of course real data will not be quite so helpful as those of Table 5.1. Even if the variables are all mutually independent we can confidently expect that random variation will cause slight deviations from the independence model. We shall develop a series of alternative models together with a means of testing them which allows for random variation.

5.3. THE FORM OF THE MODELS

Since the true population probabilities are unknown, we use the observed cell frequencies to estimate them. In consequence, what we are searching for is a model that provides a reasonable explanation of the variations that we observe in these cell frequencies. Such a model will be interpreted in terms of the cell probabilities, which must, of course, all lie between 0 and 1. Early attempts at finding models, such as those of Coleman (1964), ran into trouble because it was possible to find data sets where the estimated cell probabilities took values outside this range.

It turns out that the simplest way to formulate a model is to work not with the probabilities directly but with a function of the probabilities which is unbounded, i.e. a function whose minimum value is minus infinity and whose maximum is plus infinity. This seems an enormous leap in the dark, but it turns out that it makes life very simple.

For a dichotomous variable, for which the probabilities of categories 1 and 2 are p and $(1-p)$ respectively, we choose to work with

$$x = \log_e \left(\frac{p}{1-p} \right) \tag{5.2}$$

When $p = 0$, $x = -\infty$, when $p = 0.5$, $x = 0$, and when $p = 1$, $x = \infty$. A graphical representation of the relation between p and x, and a discussion of the use of x in the present context, is given by Theil (1971).

We can remove the logarithm in (5.2) by exponentiating both sides, when we get

$$e^x = \frac{p}{1-p}$$

which, in terms of p, gives us

$$p = \frac{1}{1+e^{-x}}. \tag{5.3}$$

The equation (5.3) shows us that each value of x relates to a unique value of p and *vice versa*, so that (5.2) provides a transformation from p with its restricted range to x with a doubly infinite range. The result of this diabolically clever mathematical trick is that whatever value we estimate for x it is certain to correspond to a valid value for p.

The function x is known as the *logit* or the *log odds*, the latter being more descriptive but the former being the term usually applied to dichotomous variables. A principal proponent of the use of the logit in a variety of situations has been Professor Berkson; see, for example, Berkson (1944). The first use of the logit with cross-classified data would seem to be by Plackett (1962).

5.4. THE SATURATED MODEL FOR A 2×2 TABLE

To see how we can formulate a model to describe all the complex interrelationships in a multidimensional table we first consider the simplest possible situation, a 2×2 table. Our arguments will be clearer if we have some real numbers to fix our ideas to, and so a hypothetical set of cell probabilities is given in Table 5.2.

Table 5.2. Hypothetical cell probabilities for 2×2 data

	B_1	B_2	Total
A_1	0·4	0·3	0·7
A_2	0·2	0·1	0·3
Total	0·6	0·4	1·0

The four cell probabilities in Table 5.2 are not all the same: our task is to identify the reasons for their deviations. There are three contributing causes, all more-or-less self-evident:

(a) Category A_1 is more common than category A_2.
(b) Category B_1 is more common than category B_2.
(c) The A_1, B_2 combination and the A_2, B_1 combination are slightly more common than would have been expected if the variables A and B had been independent.

What we require is a mathematical method which allows us to quantify the relative importance of these three effects and to detect occasions where the effects can be presumed real and occasions where the effects are merely caused by random variation.

We have suggested that such a method will involve the use of a model which has as its subject the natural logarithm v_{ij} of the cell probability p_{ij}. The model will consist of an average term, roughly equivalent to the idea of the average of the cell probabilities, together with three additive modifying terms corresponding to the three causes listed above. Such a model, suggested by Goodman (1970, 1971a), is given by

$$v_{ij} = \mu + \lambda_i^A + \lambda_j^B + \lambda_{ij}^{AB} \qquad (5.4)$$

where

$$\sum_i \lambda_i^A = \sum_j \lambda_j^B = \sum_i \lambda_{ij}^{AB} = \sum_j \lambda_{ij}^{AB} = 0$$

The terms on the right-hand side of the model (5.4) correspond in order to the overall average and to the three effects previously listed. The parameters λ (lambda) have superscripts to show to which variables they refer and subscripts to show to which category of that variable they apply.

Since there are only four cells in a 2×2 table, any workable model can have at most four distinct parameters. If the model has as many parameters as there are cells then it is called a *saturated* model. The model (5.4) is the saturated model for a 2×2 table. The four parameters could be μ, λ_1^A, λ_1^B, λ_{11}^{AB}. The restrictions on the λ's mean that

$$\lambda_2^A = -\lambda_1^A$$
$$\lambda_2^B = -\lambda_1^B$$
$$\lambda_{22}^{AB} = -\lambda_{12}^{AB} = -\lambda_{21}^{AB} = \lambda_{11}^{AB}$$

(5.5)

So, for example, an alternative set of four independent parameters might be μ, λ_2^A, λ_1^B, λ_{12}^{AB}.

To get some idea of what these λ's are, we must first introduce some simplifying notation. We write

$$v_{i\cdot} = \sum_j \frac{v_{ij}}{J}$$

$$v_{\cdot j} = \sum_i \frac{v_{ij}}{I}$$

(5.6)

$$v_{\cdot\cdot} = \sum_i \sum_j \frac{v_{ij}}{IJ}$$

with I and J being the numbers of categories for the two variables A and B. For the 2×2 case $I = J = 2$. So, for example, $v_{i\cdot}$ is the average log probability of all the cells in the ith row of the table, while $v_{\cdot\cdot}$ is the average log probability over all the cells of the table.

If we sum both sides of the model (5.4) over the suffix i (the categories of A) we get

$$\sum_i v_{ij} = \sum_i \mu + \sum_i \lambda_i^A + \sum_i \lambda_j^B + \sum_i \lambda_{ij}^{AB}$$

which, using the restrictions on the λ's, simplifies to

$$I \times v_{\cdot j} = I \times \mu + 0 + I \times \lambda_j^B + 0$$

(5.7)

Similarly, summing both sides of the model (5.4) over all the observations we get

$$IJv_{\cdot\cdot} = IJ \times \mu + 0 + 0 + 0$$

(5.8)

and hence $\mu = v_{\cdot\cdot}$. Substituting back into equation (5.7) and into similar results of this type we obtain

$$\lambda_i^A = v_{i\cdot} - v_{\cdot\cdot}$$
$$\lambda_j^B = v_{\cdot j} - v_{\cdot\cdot}$$
$$\lambda_{ij}^{AB} = v_{ij} - v_{i\cdot} - v_{\cdot j} + v_{\cdot\cdot}$$

(5.9)

This set of equations, (5.9), will be familiar to readers acquainted with analysis of variance techniques, as being direct analogues of the estimates of the parameters in a two-way model with interaction. The link between the current topic and that of the analysis of variance is very strong; a detailed review is provided by Nelder (1974), who points out that many of the standard analysis of variance techniques are easily adapted to the present situation. The interpretation of λ_i^A is seen to be, from (5.9), that additional advantage (or disadvantage) of having the particular category i for variable A, as opposed to the average value.

Some further insight is provided by expanding the equations (5.9) for the 2×2 situation, when we find that, for example,

$$\lambda_1^A = \frac{v_{11} + v_{12} - v_{21} - v_{22}}{4} = \tfrac{1}{4} \sum_j \log_e \left(\frac{p_{1j}}{p_{2j}} \right)$$

$$\lambda_1^B = \frac{v_{11} - v_{12} + v_{21} - v_{22}}{4} = \tfrac{1}{4} \sum_i \log_e \left(\frac{p_{i1}}{p_{i2}} \right) \tag{5.10}$$

$$\lambda_{11}^{AB} = \frac{v_{11} - v_{12} - v_{21} + v_{22}}{4} = \tfrac{1}{4} \log_e \left(\frac{p_{11} p_{22}}{p_{12} p_{21}} \right)$$

The right-hand expressions in (5.10), in terms of the original cell probabilities, show us that these new λ's are no more than the logarithms of the odds that we considered earlier. Thus λ_1^A is seen to be proportional to the average log odds of the cells in the first row of the table and λ_{11}^{AB} is found to be the logarithm of the odds ratio that we first encountered in Section 2.7.

Example 5.1

To illustrate what is going on in the algebra we shall work out the model for the probabilities of Table 5.2. Our first step is to convert these to log probabilities, obtaining Table 5.3. From equations (5.6) we find that

$$v_{1.} = -1.060 \quad v_{2.} = -1.956 \quad v_{.1} = 1.2625 \quad v_{.2} = -1.7535 \quad v_{..} = -1.508$$

and then, using these averages in equations (5.9), we get

$$\lambda_1^A = 0.448 \quad \lambda_1^B = 0.245 \quad \lambda_{11}^{AB} = -0.101 \quad \text{and} \quad \mu = -1.508 \tag{5.11}$$

Table 5.3. Natural logarithms of the Table 5.2 cell probabilities

	B_1	B_2
A_1	−0.916	−1.204
A_2	−1.609	−2.303

The remaining λ's are deducible from these. For dichotomous variables, such as we have here, the simple rule is to change the sign once for each subscript that differs from that of the λ calculated (see equations 5.5).

We have estimated the parameters of the saturated model which has as many parameters as cells. Naturally such a model should fit the data perfectly if our techniques have been working correctly. We can try the model (5.4) on the present data, using the calculated parameter values (5.11). Thus

$$v_{11} = \mu + \lambda_1^A + \lambda_1^B + \lambda_{11}^{AB}$$

$$= -1.508 + 0.448 + 0.245 - 0.101$$

$$= -0.916$$

which is indeed the observed value in Table 5.3.

5.5. ESTIMATING THE PARAMETERS FOR THE 2×2 SATURATED MODEL

In the last section we were concerned solely with manipulating hypothetical probabilities; we turn now to the real-life situation where we wish to interpret observed cell frequencies. As will be seen, the two situations are not essentially very different. As usual we denote the observed frequency in cell (i, j) by f_{ij} and then define

$$y_{ij} = \log_e (f_{ij}) \tag{5.12}$$

The right-hand side of equation (5.12) can be written as

$$[\log_e (f_{ij}) - \log_e (f_{00})] + \log_e (f_{00}) = \log_e\left(\frac{f_{ij}}{f_{00}}\right) + \log_e(f_{00}) = \log_e (\hat{p}_{ij}) + \text{constant} \tag{5.13}$$

The result (5.13) follows from the fact that we noted earlier, equation (2.7), that the best estimate of the unknown cell probability is the observed proportion of the data in that cell. Since the term $\log_e (f_{00})$ has a known value and is the same for all the y's, we see that the y's are very like the v's in character (with the p's replaced by their estimates, the $\hat{p}$'s).

It follows that, although we cannot determine the λ's, since we do not know the p's, we can determine their estimates, the $\hat{\lambda}$'s, by replacing the v's in equations (5.10) by the corresponding y's:

$$\hat{\lambda}_1^A = y_1. - y.. = \frac{y_{11} + y_{12} - y_{21} - y_{22}}{4}$$

$$\hat{\lambda}_1^B = y_{.1} - y.. = \frac{y_{11} - y_{12} + y_{21} - y_{22}}{4} \tag{5.14}$$

Example 5.2

The following data (Table 5.4) are taken from Crewe (1976) who extracted them from the survey data discussed by Butler and Stokes (1975).

Table 5.4. *Party supported versus sex, a 2×2 cross-classification from the Butler–Stokes survey*

	B_1 Labour	B_2 Conservative	*Total*
A_1 Males aged 21–45	222	115	337
A_2 Females aged 21–45	240	185	425
Total	462	300	762

The first stage in the analysis is to convert the raw data into log frequencies. Thus $y_{11} = \log_e (222) = 5.403$, and similarly we obtain $y_{12} = 4.745$, $y_{21} = 5.481$, and $y_{22} = 5.220$. In consequence, using equations (5.14) we obtain the following parameter estimates:

$$\hat{\lambda}_1^A = -0.138 \qquad \hat{\lambda}_1^B = 0.230 \quad \text{and} \quad \hat{\lambda}_{11}^{AB} = 0.100$$

Since we know that the saturated model should reproduce the original observations exactly, we can deduce that $\hat{\mu} = 5.212$, although this is not of immediate concern to us. What does concern us are the sizes of the λ's. We see that the most important influence on the cell frequencies is the lack of an even split in the respondent's political allegiance, the next most important effect being the sex distinction. There is, however, a relatively large $\hat{\lambda}_{11}^{AB}$ estimate, suggesting that there is a substantial association between sex and party supported. In the next section we consider methods of testing which of these effects are real and which can be attributed to random variation.

5.6. THE INDEPENDENCE MODEL FOR THE 2×2 TABLE

The saturated model (5.4) contained as many parameters as there were cells in the table and consequently fitted the cell frequencies perfectly. However, our purpose in studying models was to find a relatively parsimonious explanation of the data if at all possible. We therefore now consider a variety of simpler models, searching for the simplest model which yet provides a satisfactory explanation of the data.

From our previous work on association it is natural to consider first the following model of independence:

$$v_{ii} = \mu + \lambda_i^A + \lambda_i^B \tag{5.15}$$

We have asserted that this is a model of independence and now demonstrate this fact. The quantity v_{ij} is the natural logarithm of p_{ij} so

$$p_{ij} = \exp(\mu + \lambda_i^A + \lambda_j^B)$$

and thus

$$p_{10} = p_{11} + p_{12} = \exp(\mu + \lambda_1^A)[\exp(\lambda_1^B) + \exp(-\lambda_1^B)] \qquad (5.16)$$

remembering that for the 2×2 table $\lambda_2^A = -\lambda_1^A$, $\lambda_2^B = -\lambda_1^B$. Similarly,

$$p_{02} = p_{12} + p_{22} = \exp(\mu - \lambda_1^B)[\exp(\lambda_1^A) + \exp(-\lambda_1^A)] \qquad (5.17)$$

and

$$p_{00} = p_{10} + p_{20} = \exp(\mu)[\exp(\lambda_1^A) + \exp(-\lambda_1^A)][\exp(\lambda_1^B) + \exp(-\lambda_1^B)] \qquad (5.18)$$

Now, using these results (5.16), (5.17), and (5.18), we get

$$\frac{p_{10}p_{02}}{p_{00}} = \exp(\mu + \lambda_1^A - \lambda_1^B) = p_{12} \qquad (5.19)$$

and the identity between the left- and right-hand sides of equation (5.19) is precisely what one expects if the variables are independent. Of course, the model (5.15) and the saturated model (5.4) are identical except for the omission of λ_{ij}^{AB} from the model (5.15), so we now have further evidence that it was this term which specified the interaction between the variables.

The simplest way to fit the model (5.15) is to use the standard result (5.19) and its equivalents for the other cells. This gives us expected frequencies which are easily converted into expected log frequencies for the purposes of determining the λ's. The goodness of fit of the model can be measured using X^2 or Y^2 in the usual manner.

Example 5.3

Table 5.5. Expected frequencies and log frequencies under the hypothesis of independence for the Table 5.4 data

		B_1	B_2
A_1	Frequencies	204.3	132.7
	Log frequencies	5.320	4.888
A_2	Frequencies	257.7	167.3
	Log frequencies	5.552	5.120

As an example of the independence model (5.15) we utilize the data of Table 5.4, for which the expected frequencies and their natural logarithms are given in Table 5.5. The frequencies are obtained in the usual way, e.g. by result

(5.19), and using the results (5.14) we obtain $\hat{\mu} = 5.220$, $\hat{\lambda}_1^A = -0.116$, and $\hat{\lambda}_1^B = 0.216$.

We can calculate the goodness of fit of this model using either X^2 or Y^2. Henceforth we shall use Y^2 rather than X^2, because it has some additive properties that prove useful in the analysis. If the estimated frequencies are denoted by $\{e_{ij}\}$, then, from equation (3.5),

$$Y^2 = 2 \sum_i \sum_j f_{ij}[\log_e (f_{ij}) - \log_e (e_{ij})] \tag{5.20}$$

$$= 2[222(5.403 - 5.320) + 115(4.745 - 4.888) + 240(5.481 - 5.552)$$
$$+ 185(5.220 - 5.120)]$$

$$= 2(18.426 - 16.445 - 17.040 + 18.500)$$

$$= 6.9$$

There are three independent parameters in the model $(\mu, \lambda_1^A, \lambda_1^B)$ and four cell frequencies, so that there is 1 degree of freedom available for a test of goodness of fit of this model. Since the observed value of 6.9 is greater than the upper 1 per cent point—6.63—of a χ_1^2 distribution we are obliged to reject the hypothesis of independence: the omission of λ_{ij}^{AB} from our model has resulted in a substantial reduction in the goodness of fit. There is a tendency for females to vote Conservative and males Labour.

5.7. OTHER MODELS FOR THE 2×2 TABLE

The saturated model and the independence model are not the only possibilities. For example, we could hypothesize that the B categories were equally probable (and consequently the variables A and B were independent):

$$v_{ij} = \mu + \lambda_i^A \tag{5.21}$$

or that the A categories were equally probable:

$$v_{ij} = \mu + \lambda_j^B \tag{5.22}$$

or that all the categories were equally probable:

$$v_{ij} = \mu \tag{5.23}$$

The expected frequencies under these models are easily calculated in an obvious fashion. For example, for the model (5.21), which assumes the B categories are equiprobable,

$$e_{11} = e_{12} = e_{1.}$$

$$e_{21} = e_{22} = e_{2.}$$

where $e_{1.}$ and $e_{2.}$ are the two row averages. By taking logarithms of these expected frequencies the values of the parameter estimates are obtainable in a straightforward fashion.

Example 5.4

To amplify the discussion of the various models we recapitulate our previous results and introduce the results for the three new models in Table 5.6.

Table 5.6. Results for alternative models for Table 5.4 data

Model	Description	e_{11}	e_{12}	e_{21}	e_{22}	$\hat{\lambda}_1^A$	$\hat{\lambda}_1^B$	$\hat{\lambda}_{11}^{AB}$	$\hat{\mu}$	Degrees of freedom	Y^2
(5.4)	Saturated	222.0	115.0	240.0	185.0	−0.138	0.230	0.100	5.212	0	0
(5.15)	Independence	204.3	132.7	257.7	167.3	−0.116	0.216	0	5.220	1	6.9
(5.21)	No B effect	168.5	168.5	212.5	212.5	−0.116	0	0	5.243	2	41.7
(5.22)	No A effect	231.0	150.0	231.0	150.0	0	0.216	0	5.227	2	17.2
(5.23)	Equiprobable	190.5	190.5	190.5	190.5	0	0	0	5.250	3	51.9

We have already noted that the difference between the models (5.4) and (5.15) was simply that the former included λ_{11}^{AB}, and the test of this single parameter was a comparison of the Y^2 values: $(6.9-0)$ on $(1-0)$ degrees of freedom. The same technique can be applied to obtain specific tests of the importance of other parameters. For example, comparing the models (5.15) and (5.21) (Table 5.7) we see that, for the 1 degree of freedom corresponding to λ_1^B, we have a Y^2 contribution of 34.8, which is most highly significant.

Table 5.7. Comparison of models (5.15) and (5.21) for Table 5.4 data

Model	Parameters included	Degrees of freedom	Y^2
(5.15)	$\mu, \lambda_1^A, \lambda_1^B$	1	6.9
(5.21)	μ, λ_1^A	2	41.7
Difference	λ_1^B, given that μ and λ_1^A are fitted	1	34.8

The importance of working with the likelihood-ratio statistic Y^2, rather than the more familiar X^2, is that a subdivision such as that carried out in Table 5.7 is a theoretically valid one, which would not be the case if X^2 were used.

An alternative and equivalent point of view, in which the saturated model is built up in stages from the equiprobable model, is shown in Table 5.8.

Table 5.8. Build up of the saturated model for Table 5.4 data

Model	Parameters included	Y^2	Reduction in Y^2
(5.23)	μ	51.9	
(5.21)	μ, λ_1^A	41.7	10.2
(5.15)	$\mu, \lambda_1^A, \lambda_1^B$	6.9	34.8
(5.4)	$\mu, \lambda_1^A, \lambda_1^B, \lambda_{11}^{AB}$	0	6.9

5.8. HIERARCHICAL MODELS

All the models so far considered have been members of the class of models known as *hierarchical* models. A hierarchical model obeys the following rule, which is framed in the general multidimensional setting. Suppose that the parameter involving a set of variables S is included in the model; then the model must also include all the parameters involving any subset of S.

Example 5.5

Suppose λ_{ijk}^{ABC} is included in a (multidimensional) model. Then the following λ's must also appear: λ_i^A, λ_j^B, λ_k^C, λ_{ij}^{AB}, λ_{ik}^{AC} and λ_{jk}^{BC}.

Example 5.6

An example of a 2×2 model which does not belong to the hierarchical set is

$$v_{ij} = \mu + \lambda_{ij}^{AB} \tag{5.24}$$

and this is the sort of model that one might be tempted to fit to the data given in Table 5.9.

Table 5.9. Data displaying interaction but no main effects

	B_1	B_2	Total
A_1	70	30	100
A_2	30	70	100
Total	100	100	200

There is a manifest association between A and B in Table 5.9, and it would clearly be most misleading to state that A and B had no effect! If it were possible to subdivide these categories then we might well locate very substantial 'effects'. This is the verbal argument against fitting the model (5.24), but there is also a statistical argument. The maximum likelihood estimates that we have been using have the property that, in general, if we are fitting the parameter λ_{ijk}^{ABC} then the observed total frequencies summed over those variables will equal the expected frequencies. This has the effect that one cannot, using this method of estimation, fit λ_{ijk}^{ABC} without implicitly also fitting $\lambda_i^A, \ldots, \lambda_{jk}^{BC}$ simultaneously, and it seems unreasonable not to recognize this fact by including them explicitly in the model.

5.9. REPARAMETERIZING THE MODEL

Goodman (1971a) and Cox (1972) suggest that for multiway dichotomies it may often be possible to simplify the model by reparameterizing it. For example, we might replace the variables A and B by the variables A and C, where category C_1 contains all observations previously in cells (1, 1) or (2, 2) of the AB classification and category C_2 contains the remainder. Thus if the variables A and B were defined by

A_1　Husband votes Labour
A_2　Husband votes Conservative
B_1　Wife votes Labour
B_2　Wife votes Conservative

then the variable C, defined previously, has the interpretation

C_1　Marital harmony
C_2　Marital discord

Plackett (1974) remarks that while the original model may be considerably simplified by this procedure, *interpretation* of the resulting simplified model may be difficult.

Example 5.7

Table 5.10. Reparameterization of Table 5.9 data

	C_1	C_2	Total
A_1	70	30	100
A_2	70	30	100
Total	140	60	200

After reparameterizing the Table 5.9 data in the manner suggested earlier, we obtain Table 5.10, which requires only two parameters, μ and λ^C, in place of the original four.

CHAPTER 6

The Saturated Model for a Multiway Table

6.1. THE FRAMEWORK FOR AN ANALYSIS OF A MULTIWAY TABLE

In the previous chapter we studied the simplest possible situation that can arise with cross-classified data, namely a 2×2 table. Despite the simplicity of the data there were four distinct unsaturated hierarchical models that might have been appropriate. Goodman (1970) shows that this number rises to eighteen for a three-variable situation, to 166 for a four-variable situation, and into the thousands for five variables.

Our task is to choose one or more relatively simple models from among those available. Without some guide our task will not be easy when many variables are involved. Fortunately a guide exists: it is the saturated model. When we fit the saturated model we estimate the values of all the λ's that may ever be included in a simpler model. Some λ's will have values close to 0, indicating that they are of little importance. Our choice of unsaturated models will be governed by a desire to include those λ's that deviate appreciably from 0. However, all this is in the future (Chapter 7); for the present we deal with the problem of fitting the saturated model and interpreting the results.

6.2. THE GENERAL THREE-WAY TABLE

We commence our discussion of multiway tables by studying in some detail the three-way table. What we discover here can be easily extended to situations where more variables are involved. The three-way table consists of frequencies classified by the categories of three variables (e.g. age, sex, and political allegiance). We wish to discover what interrelations, if any, exist between these variables.

We shall label the three variables A, B, and C and suppose that they have I, J, and K categories respectively. We write p_{ijk} to be the (unknown) theoretical probability of a randomly chosen observation falling into cell (i, j, k), and let $v_{ijk} = \log_e (p_{ijk})$. An alternative way of defining p_{ijk} would be as the probability that an individual, chosen at random from the population being sampled, was found simultaneously to fall into category i for variable A, category j for variable B, and category k for variable C.

The saturated model provides a complete account of the composition of the quantities $\{v_{ijk}\}$ in terms of a grand mean, the 'main effects' of the variables A, B, and C, the three two-variable interactions AB, AC, and BC, and the three-variable interaction ABC. We discuss ABC later. As with the 2×2 case we use superscripts to denote the variables involved and subscripts to denote the categories of those variables, so that, for example, λ_{12}^{AC} refers to the association (interaction) between category 1 of variable A and category 2 of variable C. The full model is given by

$$v_{ijk} = \mu + \lambda_i^A + \lambda_j^B + \lambda_k^C + \lambda_{ij}^{AB} + \lambda_{ik}^{AC} + \lambda_{jk}^{BC} + \lambda_{ijk}^{ABC} \tag{6.1}$$

To remove redundancies in the model, so that the number of parameters is not greater than the number of cells $(I \times J \times K)$, the λ's in (6.1) are subject to the following constraints:

$$\sum_i \lambda_i^A = \sum_j \lambda_j^B = \cdots = \sum_i \lambda_{ij}^{AB} = \sum_j \lambda_{ij}^{AB} = \cdots = \sum_k \lambda_{ijk}^{ABC} = 0 \tag{6.2}$$

Although it does not appear very likely, to judge from the complexity of the model, it turns out that there is a very simple algorithm which leads to the determination of the λ's. Theoretical accounts are given by Deming and Stephan (1940) and Fienberg (1970a); down-to-earth demonstrations of the procedure in use are provided by Mosteller (1968) and Davis (1974). Furthermore, a number of separate algorithms (e.g. Haberman, 1972), and statistical packages for dealing with these models have been developed. One package in particular, *Everyman's Contingency Table Analysis* (*ECTA*), by Goodman and Fay (1973), has the joint benefits of basic simplicity and flexibility.

If we write

$$v_{\ldots} = \sum_i \sum_j \sum_k \frac{v_{ijk}}{IJK} \tag{6.3}$$

so that $v_{\ldots}$ is the grand mean of the log probabilities, and

$$v_{i\ldots} = \sum_j \sum_k \frac{v_{ijk}}{JK} \tag{6.4}$$

so that $v_{i\ldots}$ is the mean of all the log probabilities involving category i of variable A, then, by substitution of (6.1) in the right-hand sides of equations (6.3) and (6.4), we obtain

$$\lambda_i^A = v_{i\ldots} - v_{\ldots} \tag{6.5}$$

Thus λ_i^A is a measure of how much more (or less) likely category A_i is than the average A category.

We can obtain similar formulae for the other λ's; for example, if

$$v_{ij\cdot} = \sum_k \frac{v_{ijk}}{K} \qquad v_{i\cdot k} = \sum_j \frac{v_{ijk}}{J} \qquad \text{etc.}$$

then

$$\lambda_{ij}^{AB} = v_{ij\cdot} - v_{i\cdot\cdot} - v_{\cdot j\cdot} + v_{\cdot\cdot\cdot} \tag{6.6}$$

$$\lambda_{ijk}^{ABC} = v_{ijk} - v_{ij\cdot} - v_{i\cdot k} - v_{\cdot jk} + v_{i\cdot\cdot} + v_{\cdot j\cdot} + v_{\cdot\cdot k} - v_{\cdot\cdot\cdot} \tag{6.7}$$

The relation (6.6) implies that λ_{ij}^{AB} measures the extent to which the joint occurrence of the categories A_i and B_j is more or less likely than would have been expected if variables A and B had been independent. Similarly, λ_{ijk}^{ABC} measures the extent to which the interdependence of variables A and B is itself dependent on the category of variable C.

Coherent descriptions of multivariable interactions are difficult to produce. What we can say is that, if λ_{ijk}^{ABC} differs significantly from 0, then these particular categories of these variables are interrelated in a complicated fashion not explained by simple interdependencies between pairs of the variables. For a further attempt at defining interactions in simple terms see Davis (1974).

6.3. THE 2×2×2 TABLE

When the three variables A, B, and C are all dichotomies (that is $I = J = K = 2$), relations like (6.6) and (6.7) simplify considerably, and in their simplified forms they provide some further insight into the meaning of the λ's. In particular, we find that

$$\lambda_{111}^{ABC} = \lambda_{122}^{ABC} = \lambda_{212}^{ABC} = \lambda_{221}^{ABC} = -\lambda_{112}^{ABC} = -\lambda_{121}^{ABC} = -\lambda_{211}^{ABC} = -\lambda_{222}^{ABC} \tag{6.8}$$

$$= \frac{1}{8}\left[\log_e\left(\frac{p_{111}p_{221}}{p_{121}p_{211}}\right) - \log_e\left(\frac{p_{112}p_{222}}{p_{122}p_{212}}\right)\right] \tag{6.9}$$

$$= \frac{1}{8}\log_e\left(\frac{p_{111}p_{221}p_{122}p_{212}}{p_{121}p_{211}p_{112}p_{222}}\right) \tag{6.10}$$

From (6.8) we see that there is, effectively, only one independent three-variable interaction. From (6.9) we see that the value of this interaction is proportional to the difference between the logarithms of the odds ratios for the two 2×2 tables corresponding to the two categories of variable C. Equivalently, we could state that its value is (from 6.10) proportional to the logarithm of the ratio of the odds ratios. The form (6.10) also shows that rearrangement of the p's would provide equivalent representations in terms of the other factors. For example, from (6.10) we have

$$\lambda_{111}^{ABC} = \frac{1}{8}\left[\log_e\left(\frac{p_{111}p_{122}}{p_{121}p_{112}}\right) - \log_e\left(\frac{p_{211}p_{222}}{p_{221}p_{212}}\right)\right] \tag{6.11}$$

Thus λ_i^A refers to the ratio of two probabilities (the odds), λ_{ij}^{AB} refers to the ratio of these odds, and λ_{ijk}^{ABC} refers to a ratio of these ratios. A pattern has emerged!

The definition (6.10) for a three-variable interaction for the $2 \times 2 \times 2$ table was first proposed by Bartlett (1935). The generalization of (6.10) to $I \times J \times K$ tables was the work of Roy and Kastenbaum (1956), and it was not until the work of Mantel (1966) that the idea of using these λ's as the basis for a model was published.

6.4. ESTIMATION OF THE PARAMETERS OF THE SATURATED MODEL

The data for the general $I \times J \times K$ situation consists of observed frequencies $\{f_{ijk}\}$ in the various cells $\{(i, j, k)\}$ of the three-way classification. We write $y_{ijk} = \log_e (f_{ijk})$ and obtain the parameter estimates by replacing the v's in (6.6) and (6.7) by the corresponding y's. For example, the estimator of λ_{ij}^{AB} is, from (6.6),

$$\hat{\lambda}_{ij}^{AB} = y_{ij.} - y_{i..} - y_{.j.} + y_{...} \tag{6.12}$$

where

$$y_{ij.} = \sum_k \frac{y_{ijk}}{K} \qquad y_{i..} = \sum_j \sum_k \frac{y_{ijk}}{JK} \qquad \text{etc.}$$

The formulae for the $\hat{\lambda}$'s can therefore be written down very easily, but working out these values by hand would be somewhat tedious. Fortunately this is not necessary, since the computer packages mentioned earlier (e.g. ECTA) will do the hard work very quickly.

6.5. STANDARDIZED VALUES FOR THE PARAMETER ESTIMATES

We remarked in Section 6.1 that the purpose of fitting the saturated model was to gain an impression of the relative importance of the various λ's. The model is additive in the λ's so that those with values near to 0 will be of only slight importance. Equivalently, those that differ substantially from 0 will be important. What we need, therefore, is a guide as to what constitutes a substantial difference.

It is easy to see from an equation such as (6.12) that every estimate $\hat{\lambda}$ is a linear combination of the individual $\{y_{ijk}\}$. For example, for the $2 \times 2 \times 2$ case, we can rewrite equation (6.12) as follows:

$$\hat{\lambda}_{11}^{AB} = y_{11.} - y_{1..} - y_{.1.} + y_{...}$$

$$= \tfrac{1}{2}(y_{111} + y_{112}) - \tfrac{1}{4}(y_{111} + y_{112} + y_{121} + y_{122}) - \tfrac{1}{4}(y_{111} + y_{112} + y_{211} + y_{212})$$

$$+ \tfrac{1}{8}(y_{111} + y_{112} + y_{121} + y_{122} + y_{211} + y_{212} + y_{221} + y_{222})$$

$$= \tfrac{1}{8}y_{111} + \tfrac{1}{8}y_{112} - \tfrac{1}{8}y_{121} - \tfrac{1}{8}y_{122} - \tfrac{1}{8}y_{211} - \tfrac{1}{8}y_{212} + \tfrac{1}{8}y_{221} + \tfrac{1}{8}y_{222} \qquad (6.13)$$

In this particular case each of the cell frequencies is multiplied by $\pm\tfrac{1}{8}$, in general the coefficients may differ in magnitude.

Plackett (1962) has shown that the estimated variance of the natural logarithm of a Poisson frequency is approximately the reciprocal of that frequency:

$$\mathrm{var}\,(y_{ijk}) \simeq \frac{1}{f_{ijk}} \qquad (6.14)$$

We can write a general linear combination of multiples of the cell frequencies as

$$\hat{\lambda} = \sum_i \sum_j \sum_k a_{ijk} y_{ijk} \qquad (6.15)$$

where the $\{a_{ijk}\}$ are suitably chosen constants. For example, for $\hat{\lambda}^{AB}$, from equation (6.13) we have $a_{111} = a_{112} = a_{221} = a_{222} = \tfrac{1}{8}$, with the remaining a's being equal to $-\tfrac{1}{8}$.

Combining equations (6.14) and (6.15) we see that the estimated variance of $\hat{\lambda}$ is given approximately by

$$V(\hat{\lambda}) = \sum_i \sum_j \sum_k \frac{(a_{ijk})^2}{f_{ijk}} \qquad (6.16)$$

Within a particular saturated model the estimated parameter variances need not all be the same (it will depend on the number of categories that the variables have), and to put the λ's on an equal footing we standardize them, so that the standardized value $S(\hat{\lambda})$ has variance 1:

$$S(\hat{\lambda}) = \frac{\hat{\lambda}}{\sqrt{V(\hat{\lambda})}} \qquad (6.17)$$

Goodman (1971a) points out that these standardized values have an approximately normal distribution. The consequence of this is that if $\hat{\lambda}$ differs from 0 only by chance (in other words, the unknown true value of λ is 0), then the observed value of $S(\hat{\lambda})$ is an observation from the standard unit normal distribution, whose distribution function is tabulated in most standard statistical texts, and in Appendix 1.

6.6. THE SELECTION OF THE IMPORTANT λ's

Each of the standardized values that we obtain is an observation from a normal distribution with unit variance and with its mean being the corresponding λ. If that λ is 0 then the observation has arisen from the unit normal distribution. Tables of the unit normal distribution function (Appendix 1) show that about 95 per cent of all random observations from this distribution fall in the range -2 to 2.

Suppose we have a standardized value of 4. This is a long way outside the usual range. There are only two possible explanations: either we have witnessed a very rare event or the corresponding λ is not 0. We would probably prefer to believe the second of these explanations, and so a rough guide to the important λ's is that their corresponding observed standardized values lie outside the range $(-2, 2)$.

Notice that this is no more than a guide. It is *not* the case that we shall say that if an observed value lies outside $(-2, 2)$ then significant evidence has been provided that the corresponding λ differs from 0. It may differ or it may not. Part of one's reluctance to impart significance to an occurrence of this nature is that we shall always be looking at a large number of standardized values simultaneously. Although for any one in particular $(-2, 2)$ is a reasonable range, when we get, say, sixty values simultaneously, then it is most unreasonable to expect that all sixty will manage to squeeze between -2 and 2! In fact, the probability of that event is $(0.95)^{60} = 4.6$ per cent—'significantly' small!

We shall discover later that, if it is believed that some λ's are non-zero, then in general there will be other λ's which logically we simultaneously must judge to be non-zero. Consequently, we frame our conclusions at this point in a vague fashion, merely stating that the range $(-2, 2)$ should be used as the basis for a choice of a subset of the λ's which seem likely to be important.

The subsequent analysis of the resulting unsaturated models is dealt with in Chapter 7. The intention of the analysis of the saturated model is to find a suitable starting point for the subsequent analysis.

6.7. HIGHER-DIMENSIONAL TABLES

The notation of the three-dimensional table is easily extended to any number of further dimensions and requires no discussion. All the previous results remain essentially true.

There is one practical point that requires a mention. As the number of variables and the number of their categories increases, so the number of individual cells in the table increases. Quite often, in large studies, the number of cells exceeds the number of observations, so that there are large numbers of cells with zero cell frequencies. Sometimes there are theoretical reasons why certain cells cannot be occupied, and in such cases the current analysis is not valid and the methods of *quasi-independence* (Chapter 9) become applicable.

Two problems arise with genuine zero cell frequencies. The χ^2 approximations of the X^2 and Y^2 test statistics get severely strained and, unfortunately, there is not much one can do about this. More important, however, the saturated model is impossible to fit! The reason is easily seen: the estimates of the λ's are linear combinations of the y's, which are the logarithms of the cell frequencies. The logarithm of 0 is $-\infty$, and this makes life very difficult! Goodman (1970) recommends that before fitting the saturated model, the constant 0.5 should be added to every cell frequency, so that the problem is obviated. Indeed, the addition of 0.5 when fitting the saturated model is recommended *irrespective* of whether there are zero cell frequencies, since it turns out that it has certain desirable features—see Gart and Zweifel (1967) and Plackett (1974, Chapter 1).

Example 6.1

The following data are taken from a survey concerned with the 1975 British Referendum on entry into the Common Market, and were kindly supplied by Mr. D. Robertson.

There were five dichotomous variables (each of which relates to the respondent) which are as follows:

- *A* Voted in favour of entry, or did not
- *B* Identified self as Tory in February 1975, or did not
- *C* Had more than minimal legal schooling, or did not
- *D* Union member (or one of household a union member), or not
- *E* Middle class, or working class

For each variable the first-mentioned category is category 1, the second being category 2, so that, for example, 'working class' is category E_2.

There were 1636 respondents in the survey, but not all answered every question, so that 75 are excluded from the summarized data in Table 6.1.

Table 6.1. Cell frequencies for referendum data

Cell	Frequency	Cell	Frequency	Cell	Frequency	Cell	Frequency
11111	51	11121	142	11112	31	11122	62
21111	8	21121	37	21112	8	21122	23
12111	51	12121	64	12112	83	12122	57
22111	35	22121	21	22112	94	22122	54
11211	11	11221	37	11212	34	11222	61
21211	6	21221	11	21212	16	21222	24
12211	23	12221	19	12212	106	12222	99
22211	15	22221	25	22212	143	22222	110

Note. There were 75 respondents who did not answer every question.

These results were fed into the computer and analysed by implementing the statistical package ECTA, which produced both the estimated values of the λ's and the corresponding standardized values. The latter are shown in Table 6.2.

Table 6.2. Standardized values of λ estimates for Table 6.1 data

Parameter	Standardized value	Parameter	Standardized value
A	8.8	AE	2.7
B	−9.9	BC	2.5
C	3.7	BD	−7.2
D	−5.0	BE	6.7
E	−9.4	CD	0.3
AB	6.8	CE	8.5
AC	3.2	DE	2.5
AD	−0.4	ABC	0.3

Parameter	Standardized value	Parameter	Standardized value
ABD	0.4	CDE	−0.0
ABE	−1.0	ABCD	2.6
ACD	0.2	ABCE	−0.2
ACE	1.5	ABDE	−0.6
ADE	0.0	ACDE	−0.8
BCD	−2.4	BCDE	−0.0
BCE	0.4	ABCDE	1.8
BDE	−0.3		

The entries in Table 6.2 need clarification. For each λ the superscript appears in the parameter column and the standardized value corresponds to the first category of all the relevant variables. For example, 'A, 8.8' implies that $S(\lambda_1^A) = 8.8$. Similarly, we find that $S(\lambda_{11}^{AC}) = 3.2$, $S(\lambda_{1111}^{ABDE}) = -0.6$. The restrictions on the λ's enable us to deduce that, for example, $S(\lambda_2^A) = -8.8$, $S(\lambda_{12}^{AC}) = -3.2$, $S(\lambda_{1221}^{ABDE}) = -0.6$, etc.

Studying the absolute magnitudes of the standardized values gives us an idea of the relative importance of the different effects. We cannot know which of these values are subject to large random discrepancies but, so far as we can tell, the important effects are the following:

$$B, E, A, CE, BD, AB, BE, D, C, AC, AE, ABCD, BC, DE, \text{ and } BCD$$

These therefore are the effects that we shall initially incorporate in a simpler (unsaturated) model which we hope will provide a reasonable explanation of the data.

6.8. INTERPRETATION OF THE MODEL

Our analysis so far has been of mathematical theory rather than of practical relevance. We shall now attempt to explore the practical implications of the results.

Our first question must concern the motivation for the collection of the data. Often, data are collected on a large number of variables simultaneously, so that a costly follow-up survey can be avoided. If this is the case, then many of the variables will be of only peripheral interest in the context of a particular enquiry, and we shall presume that all the variables involved in a multiway classification are of genuine relevance to the analysis.

The variables in an analysis are of two types, which we shall label as factors and responses. The distinction between them is often temporal and is always one of cause and effect; because an individual belongs to a particular category of a certain factor variable then this makes him more likely to belong to a particular category of a response variable. Sometimes the distinction is clear cut; e.g. if a respondent is a member of the working class then he is more likely to support the Labour Party. On other occasions we may be less sure which variable is a factor and which a response; e.g. the variables 'supports the Conservative Party' and 'went to a private school'.

The analysis of a multiway table is logically different depending on which variables are factors and how many factors there are; see Bhapkar and Koch (1968) and Goodman (1971a, 1973a, 1973b). We enlarge on these differences when considering alternative unsaturated models in the next chapter.

Example 6.1 (continued)

Of the five variables under consideration in the data of Table 6.1, the variable A is clearly the unique response, since the object of our analysis is to determine which factors had a bearing on a respondent's vote for or against entry into the Common Market.

The four factors B, E, D, and C appeared, according to our model, to be in the order of importance given. The statistical analysis gave not only the standardized values of the parameters but also their unstandardized values, which were

$$\lambda_1^B = -0.351 \qquad \lambda_1^E = -0.332 \qquad \lambda_1^D = -0.179 \quad \text{and} \quad \lambda_1^C = 0.132$$

We can transform these into odds by 'antilogging', which for natural logarithms is equivalent to exponentiating, so that, for example, the odds on category B_2 as opposed to B_1 are estimated by the model as $\exp(0.351):\exp(-0.351)$, that is as $2.02:1$. The complete set of estimated odds for these four factors is given in Table 6.3, together with the actual category total obtained from Table 6.1, and the corresponding 'raw' odds. Notice that the odds between the categories of factors B and E as estimated from the model differ considerably from the raw odds derived from the marginal single-factor category totals. The reason is that the raw odds take no account of the other influences in the table—specifically the highly significant CE, BD, AB, and BE interactions—and we have seen in Section 4.2 how this can lead to mistaken conclusions. This is where the model is of real value. It sorts out for us all the major influences on the data simultaneously, and gives us a guide to their relative importance. It is, for example, no longer necessary to reduce a $2 \times 2 \times 2 \times 2 \times 2$ table to a set of ten 2×2 tables and to analyse each subtable separately, hoping meanwhile not to have lost any of the essential characteristics of the data. We can now look at the whole scenario simultaneously with complete confidence.

Table 6.3. The categories of the factors for Table 6.1 data

Factor	Category 1 frequency	Category 2 frequency	Raw odds	Estimated odds
B	562	999	1:1.78	1:2.02
E	556	1005	1:1.81	1:1.94
D	715	846	1:1.18	1:1.43
C	821	740	1.11:1	1.30:1

The model showed that the most important interactions were those between C and E and between B and D. We can reconstruct from Table 6.1 the appropriate two-way tables of marginal frequencies; these are given in Table 6.4, together with the corresponding tables of expected frequencies if the pairs of factors had been independent.

We see from Table 6.4 that there were 117 more respondents in each of the (1, 1) and (2, 2) cells for the CE subtable and 92 less respondents in the corresponding cells of the BD subtable than would have been expected under independence. Thus the association between C and E is positive, while that between B and D is negative (compare with the signs of the standardized contrasts in Table 6.2).

A more detailed analysis of these data is given in the following chapter. Our purpose here is simply to link the λ's to features of the data.

By treating the variable A as the unique response we are focussing attention on this variable and recognizing that the interrelationships between the factor variables are only of secondary interest. We can usefully bring out the direction of primary interest by recasting the $2 \times 2 \times 2 \times 2 \times 2$ table as a 2×16 two-way table, as shown in Table 6.5. The analysis is unaffected by the new format of the data.

Table 6.4. The CE and BD marginal tables for Table 6.1 data

	Observed frequencies					
	E_1	E_2			D_1	D_2
C_1	409	412		B_1	165	397
C_2	147	593		B_2	550	449

	Expected frequencies under independence					
	E_1	E_2			D_1	D_2
C_1	292	529		B_1	257	305
C_2	264	476		B_2	458	541

Table 6.5. Table 6.1 recast as a 2×16 two-way table

		Factor category combinations															
	B	1	2	1	2	1	2	1	2	1	2	1	2	1	2	1	2
	C	1	1	2	2	1	1	2	2	1	1	2	2	1	1	2	2
	D	1	1	1	1	2	2	2	2	1	1	1	1	2	2	2	2
	E	1	1	1	1	1	1	1	1	2	2	2	2	2	2	2	2
Response	A_1	51	51	11	23	142	64	37	19	31	83	34	106	62	57	61	99
category	A_2	8	35	6	15	37	21	11	25	8	94	16	143	23	54	24	110

CHAPTER 7

Unsaturated Models for a Multiway Table

7.1. THE RELATION BETWEEN THE λ'S AND THE MARGINAL TOTALS

We have already met some unsaturated models in Sections 5.6 and 5.7 when we were analysing a 2×2 table. The estimated cell frequencies for five alternative models were summarized in Table 5.6, and we use those results as a guide to some useful general relationships.

Observe that for the model of uniformity (5.23), $v_{ij} = \mu$, the four estimated cell frequencies $\{e_{ij}\}$ were all equal to one-quarter of the observed total frequency so that their sum, e_{00}, was equal to the observed total frequency, f_{00}. Likewise, for the model involving dependence on A alone (5.21), $v_{ij} = \mu + \lambda_i^A$, the cell frequencies in row i were obtained by dividing the observed row total, f_{i0}, by 2. Consequently, the sum of the estimated cell frequencies in row i, e_{i0}, is equal to the sum of the observed cell frequencies, f_{i0}. Since $e_{00} = e_{10} + e_{20}$ and $f_{00} = f_{10} + f_{20}$, it follows that $e_{00} = f_{00}$ for this model also.

Thus for a model involving μ, $e_{00} = f_{00}$, and for a model involving λ_i^A, $e_{i0} = f_{i0}$. This correspondence between the relevant estimated and observed marginal totals and the parameters being fitted in the model is not restricted to these simple situations but is (Birch, 1963) quite general. For example, suppose A, B, C, and D are four dichotomous variables, with f_{ijkl} being a typical cell frequency. Suppose that the only three-variable interaction in our (unsaturated) model is λ_{ijk}^{ABC}. If we denote the corresponding estimated cell frequencies by $\{e_{ijkl}\}$, then Birch shows that

$$\sum_l e_{ijkl} = \sum_l f_{ijkl} \qquad \text{for all } i, j, k \qquad (7.1)$$

because λ_{ijk}^{ABC} is in the model. Notice that while equation (7.1) is necessarily true, it is *not* necessarily true that, for instance,

$$\sum_i e_{ijkl} = \sum_i f_{ijkl} \qquad \text{for all } j, k, l$$

because the parameter λ_{jkl}^{BCD} is not included in the model. For example, it can be seen in Table 5.6 that under model (5.21) the column totals were not the same for the observed and expected frequencies.

70

There is a most important corollary to this general relation which can be deduced from our particular example (7.1). Suppose that we sum the left- and right-hand sides of (7.1) over all categories of variable A; then we obtain the following result:

$$e_{1jk0} + e_{2jk0} + \cdots + e_{Ijk0} = f_{1jk0} + f_{2jk0} + \cdots + f_{Ijk0}$$

that is

$$e_{0jk0} = f_{0jk0} \qquad \text{for all } j, k \qquad (7.2)$$

Because of Birch's general result we know that we get identity between marginal totals of expected and observed frequencies when the corresponding λ is included in the model. So, by including λ_{ijk}^{ABC} in the model we are also, in effect, including λ_{jk}^{BC}. Similarly, by summing the sides of equation (7.1) over the categories of the appropriate variables we see that we can also obtain the relations equivalent to the fitting of μ, λ^A, λ^B, λ^C, λ^{AB}, and λ^{AC}.

These results show that if we wish to include λ^{ABC} in the model then we must also include (albeit somewhat inadvertently) all the λ's whose superscripts are subsets of the letters A, B, and C. We cannot fit the simple model

$$v_{ijk} = \mu + \lambda_{ijk}^{ABC}$$

without implicitly fitting the other six λ's as well. Analogous situations occur in both regression and the analysis of variance.

7.2 SOME EXAMPLES OF HIERARCHICAL MODELS

The implication of fitting a high-order interaction is, as we have just seen, that a whole family of other effects and interactions are also forced to appear in the model. We can explain the causation in simple stages by stating that λ_{ijk}^{ABC} implies λ_{ij}^{AB}, λ_{ik}^{AC}, and λ_{jk}^{BC}, while λ_{ij}^{AB} implies λ_i^A and λ_j^B, and so on. In this way we build up a hierarchy of causation and hence models formed in this way are called *hierarchical models*.

Before continuing our discussion we simplify our notation. Henceforth we write ABC instead of λ_{ijk}^{ABC}. We now illustrate the implications of including various λ's in a model by reference to a five-variable situation in which the variables are labelled A to E. Thus

$$A \Rightarrow \mu, A$$

$$AB \Rightarrow \mu, A, B, AB$$

$$ABC \Rightarrow \mu, A, B, AB, C, AC, BC, ABC$$

Also, we can write down quite simply the joint implications of more than one λ being included in the model. Thus

$$A, BCE \Rightarrow \mu, A, B, C, E, BC, BE, CE, BCE$$

$$AE, BC, CDE \Rightarrow \mu, A, B, C, D, E, AE, BC, CD, CE, DE, CDE$$

Because certain λ's are automatically specified by other λ's, it follows that we can specify a complicated model by simply stating an appropriate subset. For example, if we happen to wish to fit the model containing the parameters μ, A, B, C, D, E, AE, BC, CD, CE, DE, and CDE, then we do not have to write all these down, but can simply state that we wish to fit the model implied by including AE, BC, and CDE. Most models can therefore be defined in a relatively economical fashion.

A useful system for keeping track of which parameters are included in a particular model is to keep a tally chart such as that shown in Table 7.1, which lists all the possible models for a three-variable classification.

Table 7.1. Tally chart for the nineteen possible models for a three-variable table

Defining set	μ	A	B	C	AB	AC	BC	ABC
ABC	√	√	√	√	√	√	√	√
AB/AC/BC	√	√	√	√	√	√	√	
AB/AC	√	√	√	√	√	√		
BC/AB	√	√	√	√	√		√	
AC/BC	√	√	√	√		√	√	
A/BC	√	√	√	√			√	
B/AC	√	√	√	√		√		
C/AB	√	√	√	√	√			
BC	√		√	√			√	
AC	√	√		√		√		
AB	√	√	√		√			
A/B/C	√	√	√	√				
A/B	√	√	√					
A/C	√	√		√				
B/C	√		√	√				
A	√	√						
B	√		√					
C	√			√				
μ	√							

7.3. TESTING THE SIGNIFICANCE OF AN INDIVIDUAL λ

To fit a particular model for a set of data using one of the computer packages it suffices to prescribe the defining set of parameters and then, as it were, to press the appropriate button. Not only is the model fitted but also the X^2 and Y^2 goodness-of-fit statistics are calculated automatically. The Y^2 values of alternative models provide the basis for a test of the significance of individual λ's, the method being that already outlined in Section 5.7.

We now give an example based on Table 7.1 for the $2 \times 2 \times 2$ table. Suppose that having fitted the saturated model to the data (with each cell frequency incremented by 0.5; see Section 6.7) the results suggested that the interactions AB and AC together with the main effects (A, B, C) were necessary. Consequently, we fit the model defined by AB/AC and obtain a value of Y^2, Y_1^2, say, based on 2 degrees of freedom (2 because there are two parameters not in the present model which were in the saturated model).

Suppose that we want to try the simpler model from which the AC interaction has been excluded. This is the model defined by AB/C: all the parameters in the AB/AC model occur in the AB/C model with the exception of AC. Our new value of Y^2 is Y_2^2 based on 3 degrees of freedom, since there are now three parameters omitted from the saturated model.

The difference between the two models is the exclusion of AC from the second model, which has resulted in 1 extra degree of freedom and an increase in the value of Y^2 from Y_1^2 to Y_2^2. The situation is summarized in Table 7.2. Common sense tells us that if all the changes are due to the AC interaction then the importance of that interaction can be guaged from studying the value of the difference $(Y_2^2 - Y_1^2)$, which turns out to have a χ^2 distribution with $(3-2)=1$ degree of freedom. If the difference exceeds an appropriately large value, e.g. the upper 5 per cent. significance point of the χ^2 distribution, then we argue that leaving the parameter out of the model makes a correspondingly significant difference.

Table 7.2. Comparison of models for $2 \times 2 \times 2$ table

Model	Defining set	Parameters included	Degrees of freedom	Y^2
1	AB/AC	μ, A, B, C, AB, AC	2	Y_1^2
2	AB/C	μ, A, B, C, AB	3	Y_2^2
Difference		AC, with μ, A, B, C, AB occurring in both models	1	$Y_2^2 - Y_1^2$

In more complex situations, i.e. with more than three variables, it is possible to find a variety of pairs of models which differ only by the same single parameter. The differences in the Y^2 values within these pairs will not all be identical, so we need to be clear that our test is a test for the significance of a particular parameter *given* that a certain set of other parameters have been included. For example, in Table 7.2, we were testing the importance of AC given that μ, A, B, C, and AB were being fitted. We shall refer later (Section 8.1) to work by Brown (1976) which relates to this point.

One reservation that needs stating in connection with the method of analysis that we are using is that the χ^2 distributions to which we continually refer are no more than good approximations. That is, the distributions of our test statistics, when the numbers of observations involved are reasonably large, are approximately χ^2. The use of the distribution as an approximation for X^2 has been investigated by a number of authors (see, for example, Yarnold, 1970) and seems to work well even for small cell frequencies. Williams (1976) has investigated the distribution of Y^2 for log-linear models such as we are studying, and provides a correction factor which improves the accuracy of the χ^2 approximation. However, the extra calculations are unlikely to be worth while in practice, since we are not seeking law-like relations but rather a guide as to the relations that exist.

7.4. AN ANALYSIS OF A FIVE-FACTOR TABLE

We have already remarked that the variables involved in a cross-classification are of two types, factors and responses. If all the variables are regarded as factors then the analysis centres on locating the interrelations between these factors. Essentially, the situation is one of locating correlations rather than of regression. To exemplify the method of analysis for this situation we shall treat the referendum data of Table 6.1 as though variable A were a factor and not a response. In Section 7.7 we reanalyse the data with A considered as a response.

We have already completed the first stage of our analysis by fitting the saturated model to the data, and the standardized λ values were given in Table 6.2. The next stage in the analysis is to fit an unsaturated model. Scanning the four-factor interactions first (because if any of these are included then, as we have seen, the hierarchical nature of the models means that many simpler effects must also be included), we see that all except $ABCD$ have values close to 0. However, the standardized value for $ABCD$ is 2.6, which is quite high (remembering the approximate usual range of -2 to 2), and we could reasonably decide to include this in our preliminary unsaturated model. Automatically therefore we also include ABC, ABD, ACD, BCD, AB, AC, AD, BC, BD, CD, A, B, C, D, and μ. The only effects not already included are those involving E. There are no three-factor interactions involving E which exceed 2 in magnitude, so we decide not to include any in our model, but all four of the two-factor interactions (AE, BE, CE, and DE) appear important, and of course E is also included.

The resulting model with its twenty-one parameters is shown in Table 7.3 as model 1. Using a computer package such as ECTA we simply specify the defining set of parameters, which is $ABCD/AE/BE/CE/DE$, and the computer does the rest. The value of Y^2 is 9.87 which is a typical value for an observation from a χ^2_{11} distribution. Thus the very first model that we have tried provides an adequate explanation of the data.

It is worth recalling at this stage the reason that we are investigating possible unsaturated models, which is that if a comparatively simple explanation of the observed cell frequencies can be found then this may provide useful insight. Model 1 has 11 degrees of freedom and therefore there are eleven parameters less in this model than in the saturated model (namely $ABCDE$, $BCDE$, $ACDE$, $ABDE$, $ABCE$, CDE, BDE, BCE, ADE, ACE, and ABE). To this extent we have simplified our model, but it still contains a further twenty-one parameters, and so we would like, if possible, to find a still more parsimonious model, with even fewer parameters which will be correspondingly simpler to interpret.

The prime candidate for assassination is the four-factor interaction $ABCD$, since its presence in the model implies, as we have seen earlier, that there are fourteen other λ's which have to be included. Model 2, despite the apparent extra complexity of its defining set of fitted margins, actually includes all the parameters of model 1 with the exception of $ABCD$, and with no additional parameters. The resultant Y^2 value of 14.26 is therefore, if the model fits the data, an observation from a χ^2 distribution with 12 degrees of freedom. The observed value is fairly typical of the distribution and we can accept that model 2 is an alternative explanation of the data. The difference from model 1 is the omission of $ABCD$ and it is therefore $ABCD$ which is associated with the extra degree of freedom, and with the increase in the Y^2 value from 9.87 to 14.26, an increase of 4.39. Since the upper 5 per cent. significance point of a χ^2_1 distribution is 3.84, which is less than 4.39, it follows that we have observed a somewhat unlikely value, and we would generally prefer to reject the hypothesis that $ABCD = 0$ in favour of the alternative that $ABCD \neq 0$.

Since it appears that we should continue to include $ABCD$, we next test the models which omit the other possible candidates for omission, AE, BE, CE and DE. These are models 3 to 6. In each case there is very clear evidence that these parameters are needed—none of these four models provides a good fit to the data. It therefore appears that there is no single parameter which can be omitted from model 1 without a significant worsening of the fit.

We now consider whether it is possible to find any further parameters which when included in the model provide a significant improvement to the fit. The obvious candidates are the three-factor interactions involving E, none of which appeared in model 1. Models 7 to 12 illustrate the results of including each of these, in turn, in the model. In no case is there a significant improvement in the goodness of fit; the best, ACE, produces a decrease in the Y^2 value of only 2.73, which is considerably less than 3.84, the upper 5 per cent point of the χ^2_1 distribution.

Table 7.3. Possible unsaturated models for Table 6.1 data

Model number	Defining set	Degrees of freedom	Y^2	Parameter under test	Result of test
1	ABCD/AE/BE/CE/DE	11	9.87	Model	Model fits well
2	ABC/ABD/ACD/BCD/AE/BE/CE/DE	12	14.26	ABCD	Significant at 5.0% level
3	ABCD/BE/CE/DE	12	23.46	AE	Significant at 0.1% level
4	ABCD/AE/CE/DE	12	65.16	BE	Significant at 0.1% level
5	ABCD/AE/BE/DE	12	125.35	CE	Significant at 0.1% level
6	ABCD/AE/BE/CE	12	20.35	DE	Significant at 0.5% level
7	ABCD/ABE/CE/DE	10	9.05	ABE	Not significant
8	ABCD/ACE/BE/DE	10	7.14	ACE	Not significant
9	ABCD/ADE/BE/CE	10	9.76	ADE	Not significant
10	ABCD/AE/BCE/DE	10	9.45	BCE	Not significant
11	ABCD/AE/CE/BDE	10	9.85	BDE	Not significant
12	ABCD/AE/BE/CDE	10	9.83	CDE.	Not significant
2	ABC/ABD/ACD/BCD/AE/BE/CE/DE	12	14.26	Model	Model fits well
13	ABC/ABD/BCD/AE/BE/CE/DE	13	14.39	ACD	Not significant
14	AC/ABD/BCD/AE/BE/CE/DE	14	14.41	ABC	Not significant
15	AC/AB/AD/BCD/AE/BE/CE/DE	15	16.07	ABD	Not significant
16	AC/AB/BCD/AE/BE/CE/DE	16	17.24	AD	Not significant
17	AC/AB/BC/BD/CD/AE/BE/CE/DE	17	20.97	BCD	Not significant
18	AC/AB/BC/BD/AE/BE/CE/DE	18	22.32	CD	Not significant
18	AB/AC/AE/BC/BD/BE/CE/DE	18	22.32	Model	Model fits well
19	AC/AE/BC/BD/BE/CE/DE	19	92.90	AB	Significant at 0.1% level
20	AB/AE/BC/BD/BE/CE/DE	19	28.58	AC	Significant at 2.5% level

Table 7.3 (*continued*)

Model number	Defining set	Degrees of freedom	Y^2	Parameter under test	Result of test
21	$AB/AC/BC/BD/BE/CE/DE$	19	36.74	AE	Significant at 0.1% level
22	$AB/AC/AE/BD/BE/CE/DE$	19	32.61	BC	Significant at 0.5% level
23	$AB/AC/AE/BC/BE/CE/DE$	19	79.04	BD	Significant at 0.1% level
24	$AB/AC/AE/BC/BD/CE/DE$	19	96.77	BE	Significant at 0.1% level
25	$AB/AC/AE/BC/BD/BE/DE$	19	137.08	CE	Significant at 0.1% level
26	$AB/AC/AE/BC/BD/BE/CE$	19	32.82	DE	Significant at 0.5% level
27	$ABC/AE/BD/BE/CE/DE$	17	22.31	ABC	Not significant
28	$ABE/AC/BC/BD/CE/DE$	17	21.28	ABE	Not significant
29	$ACE/AB/BC/BD/BE/DE$	17	19.65	ACE	Not significant
30	$BCE/AB/AC/AE/BD/DE$	17	21.69	BCE	Not significant
31	$BDE/AB/AC/AE/BC/CE$	17	22.05	BDE	Not significant

We are left therefore with model 1, a model which fits the data well, which cannot be improved significantly by the addition of any single parameter and which is worsened significantly by the remov . of any of the possible parameters. This looks like the end of the road! However, let us reconsider our decision concerning the parameter $ABCD$. Our test result was interpreted as an indication that the true value of $ABCD$ differed from 0, the alternative being that we had observed a value so large as to occur only about once in twenty-five occasions. Could this be the twenty-fifth occasion? We cannot tell, but we can conjecture. If there is a real four-factor interaction involving A, B, C, and D, then we could reasonably expect that the three-factor interactions ACD, ABC, ABD, and BCD should also be sizeable. Reference to Table 6.2 shows that while BCD is sizeable, the remaining three are not. It is therefore tempting, in an effort to achieve a simple explanation of the data, to try dropping these parameters out of the model and to see what happens.

Model 13 contains all the parameters of model 2, except for ACD; the increase in Y^2 is very small. Models 14 to 18 remove further parameters, in each case without a significant increase in the value of Y^2. Model 18 contains only fourteen parameters, but still provides a good fit to the data. We compare the fit of model 18 with that of model 1 in Table 7.4. The seven extra

Table 7.4. Comparison of models 1 and 18

Model	Parameters fitted	Degrees of freedom	Y^2
18	μ, A, B, C, D, E, AB, AC, AE, BC, BD, BE, CE, and DE	18	22.32
1	Those for model 18 plus ABCD, ABC, ABD, ACD, BCD, AD, CD	11	9.87
Difference	ABCD, ABC, ABD, ACD, BCD, AD, CD, given the fit of those specified for model 18	7	12.45

parameters in model 1 improve the fit; the value of Y^2 is reduced by 12.45. However, consultation of tables of the percentage points of a χ_7^2 distribution reveals that a value as large or larger than 12.45 could be expected to occur by chance roughly 10 per cent of the time.

Models 19 to 26 attempt to simplify model 18 still further, but all the remaining parameters are clearly most important. The least important is seen to be AC, but the relevant model, model 20, provides a rather poor fit to the data. Models 27 to 31 test whether there is any single parameter which can be included with those of model 18 which will provide a significant improvement, but none can be found.

Table 7.5. Parameter estimates under models 1 and 18

Effect	Model 1	Model 18
Grand mean	3.558	3.567
A	0.331	0.319
B	−0.361	−0.357
C	0.145	0.169
D	−0.189	−0.190
E	−0.338	−0.338
AB	0.255	0.249
AC	0.093	0.070
AD	−0.017	0
AE	0.114	0.117
BC	0.082	0.096
BD	−0.255	−0.246
BE	0.228	0.229
CD	−0.012	0
CE	0.313	0.311
DE	−0.097	−0.093
ABC	0.012	0
ABD	0.039	0
ACD	0.024	0
BCD	−0.083	0
ABCD	0.068	0

Table 7.6. *The observed frequencies and their estimated values for various models*

Cell	Observed	Model 1	Model 18	Model 38	Two-stage Model
11111	51	49.9	48.6	48.3	49.8
21111	8	7.9	11.0	10.7	11.0
12111	51	51.5	52.5	53.8	52.7
22111	35	36.5	31.4	32.2	31.5
11211	11	13.8	13.6	13.2	13.2
21211	6	4.8	4.0	3.8	3.9
12211	23	19.5	21.1	21.2	21.2
22211	15	16.0	16.8	16.8	16.8
11121	142	142.0	142.7	146.7	143.1
21121	37	35.5	31.5	32.3	31.6
12121	64	58.0	56.5	53.2	55.9
22121	21	27.6	33.8	31.8	33.5
11221	37	38.8	39.2	37.1	39.1
21221	11	10.2	11.5	10.9	·11.4
12221	19	24.6	22.8	24.5	23.1
22221	25	19.3	18.1	19.5	18.4
11112	31	32.1	31.6	28.8	33.3
21112	8	8.1	11.1	10.2	11.7
12112	83	82.5	83.6	90.5	87.5
22112	94	92.5	79.8	86.5	83.5
11212	34	31.5	30.1	34.1	28.7
21212	16	17.2	14.1	15.9	13.4
12212	106	109.5	116.8	109.8	113.3
22212	143	142.0	148.0	139.2	143.6
11122	62	62.0	62.6	62.9	60.3
21122	23	24.5	22.0	22.1	21.2
12122	57	63.0	62.0	56.8	58.5
22122	54	47.4	59.3	54.2	55.9
11222	61	59.2	59.7	57.9	61.6
21222	24	24.8	27.9	27.1	28.8
12222	99	93.4	86.7	92.2	89.8
22222	110	115.7	109.8	116.8	113.9
Degrees of freedom		11	18	12	16
Y^2 value		9.87	22.32	16.48	20.57

Of the thirty-one models that we have considered, nineteen provide reasonable explanations for the data. Of the nineteen, two stand out, namely models 1 and 18. Which of these models we should choose depends upon the reason for our wanting a model at all, and on any prior ideas we may have concerning the likely interrelations between the factors. To get an idea of the extent to which the models differ, we give the estimated parameter values for models 1 and 18 in Table 7.5 and the corresponding estimated frequencies in Table 7.6.

It can be seen from Table 7.5 that the differences in the parameter estimates under the two models are relatively small. This is reassuring, since it suggests that it may not make a great deal of difference which model we choose from a number of more-or-less equally successful models. Note that the values given are the unstandardized values: to obtain the standardized values it is necessary (in this case) to divide each value by 0.036.

The values given in·Table 7.6 are those of the observed frequencies in the thirty-two cells and the estimated frequencies under the two models and under a two-stage model discussed in Section 7.9. For all the models it can be seen that the principal contributions to the lack of fit come from the two cells (2, 2, 2, 2, 1)—underestimated by the models—and (2, 2, 1, 2, 1)—overestimated by the models. The estimated frequencies are derived directly from the parameter estimates of Table 7.5. We illustrate the method of calculation below, although in practice the values are calculated automatically by the computer.

Model 18 states that the log probability of cell (i, j, k, l, m) is given by

$$v_{ijklm} = \mu + \lambda_i^A + \lambda_j^B + \lambda_k^C + \lambda_l^D + \lambda_m^E + \lambda_{ij}^{AB} + \lambda_{ik}^{AC} + \lambda_{im}^{AE} + \lambda_{jk}^{BC} + \lambda_{jl}^{BD} + \lambda_{jm}^{BE}$$
$$+ \lambda_{km}^{CE} + \lambda_{lm}^{DE}$$

with the estimated magnitudes of the parameters being those of Table 7.5. The signs of the $\hat{\lambda}$'s are determined by the suffices. For every 2 suffix the value given should be multiplied by -1. For example, $\hat{\lambda}_{12}^{DE} = (-0.093) \times 1 \times (-1) = 0.093$, whereas $\hat{\lambda}_{11}^{AB} = 0.249 \times 1 \times 1 = 0.249$. Consequently, the estimated log frequency in, for example, cell (2, 2, 1, 2, 1) is

$$3.567 + (-0.319) + 0.357 - (-0.169) + 0.190 - 0.338 + 0.249$$

$$-0.070 - 0.117 - 0.096 + (-0.246) - 0.229 + 0.311 - (-0.093) = 3.521$$

and thus the estimated frequency in this cell is $e^{3.521} = 33.8$, which is the figure given in Table 7.6.

We postpone further discussion of the referendum data until section 7.6, where we reanalyse the data treating variable A as the single response variable. First, however, we review what we have learnt so far.

7.5. DISCUSSION OF THE TECHNIQUES EMPLOYED IN THE HUNT FOR A SUITABLE MODEL

It should, perhaps, be remarked at the outset that the discussion in the previous section has probably taken the reader longer to read than it took the author to derive the results using the computer package ECTA.

Table 7.3 shows quite clearly that there were two basic techniques employed in the hunt for a simple model. These methods, which are familiar to those faced with multiple regression problems (see, for example, Draper and Smith, 1966) are *forward selection*, in which at each stage the next most important λ is included in the model, and *backward elimination*, in which, at each stage, the least important λ is excluded from the model. Hocking (1976), in a discussion of the regression situation, points out that neither method, nor any combination of these two methods, will necessarily lead to the unique best model—if, indeed, such a model exists. We only obtained the relatively simple model 18 by 'bending the rules', albeit in a sensible fashion.

Goodman (1971a, p. 41) summarizes the position thus: 'By including additional λ's in the model, the fit can be improved; and so the researcher must weigh in each particular case the advantages of the improved fit against the disadvantages of having introduced additional parameters in the model. Different researchers will weigh these advantages and disadvantages differently.'

7.6. HANDLING A MIXED FACTOR AND RESPONSE SITUATION

When one or more of the variables is a response rather than a factor, then our interest is focused on the way that this response variable is affected by the factor variables. The direct effects of the factors and their interactions are not of primary concern. The theory for these mixed situations depends on how many response variables there are; see Bhapkar and Koch (1968). Goodman (1971a) shows how our previous method of analysis should be adapted to deal with this new situation. The argument is that the differences in the cell frequencies due to the factor effects and the interactions between these factors should be regarded as a fact of life. The object of the analysis is to identify further variations due to the response variable and its interactions with the various factors. Consequently, we consider *only* those models in which all the factor interactions are included. For example, if A and B are factors and C and D are responses, then every model that we consider contains the AB, A, and B parameters, irrespective of their apparent significance.

Subject to this restriction our methods of selection are the same as for the multifactor situation.

7.7. EXAMPLE OF THE MIXED FACTOR/RESPONSE SITUATION

To illustrate the adaption of the methodology to the mixed factor/response situation, we reanalyse the referendum data of Table 6.1, recognizing that variable A—whether a respondent voted in favour of the Common Market or not—is a response. The remaining variables are considered to be factors, so that all models that we fit will include $BCDE$ as a member of the defining set of parameters.

From Table 6.2 we see that there are five sizeable effects involving A, namely A (8.8), AB (−6.8), AC (3.2), AE (2.7), and $ABCD$ (2.6). We therefore try as a first model (model 32 in Table 7.7) that model defined by $BCDE/ABCD/AE$, which embodies all the factor interactions and all the large interactions involving the response variable A. The results are given in Table 7.7, where we see that this model provides an excellent fit to the data.

Owing to the hierarchical constraints on the parameters there are only two single parameters that can be omitted from the model; these are $ABCD$ and AE, which are tested with models 33 and 34. Comparison of models 32 and 34 shows that the omission of AE causes an increase in Y^2 of 13.48, and we can safely conclude that AE must be retained. However, although the

Table 7.7. Unsaturated models for the mixed factor/response analysis of Table 6.1 data

Model number	Defining set	Degrees of freedom	Y^2	Parameter under test	Result of test
32	$BCDE/ABCD/AE$	7	9.26	Model	Model fits well
33	$BCDE/ABC/ABD/ACD/AE$	8	13.48	$ABCD$	Significant at 5% level
34	$BCDE/ABCD$	8	22.74	AE	Significant at 0.1% level
35	$BCDE/ABC/ABD/AE$	9	13.61	ACD	Not significant
36	$BCDE/ABD/AC/AE$	10	13.64	ABC	Not significant
37	$BCDE/AB/AD/AC/AE$	11	15.31	ABD	Not significant
38	$BCDE/AB/AC/AE$	12	16.48	AD	Not significant
38	$BCDE/AB/AC/AE$	12	16.48	Model	Model fits well
39	$BCDE/AB/AE$	13	22.80	AC	Significant at 2.5% level
40	$BCDE/AB/AC$	13	30.96	AE	Significant at 0.1% level
41	$BCDE/AC/AE$	13	87.12	AB	Significant at 0.1% level
42	$BCDE/ABC/AE$	11	16.45	ABC	Not significant
43	$BCDE/ABE/AC$	11	15.34	ABE	Not significant
44	$BCDE/ACE/AB$	11	14.25	ACE	Not significant

increase in Y^2 of 4.22 caused by the omission of $ABCD$ (model 33) exceeds 3.84, which is the 5 per cent. significance point of a χ_1^2 distribution, we are tempted to allow this omission, for the same reasons as in Section 7.4.

Successively we remove further parameters arriving at the comparatively simple model 38, which still provides an adequate explanation of the way factors B, C, D, and E influence the response A, while using five less parameters than model 32. Models 39 to 41 reveal that no further parameters can be omitted, while models 42 to 44 reveal that the introduction of extra parameters does not produce any significant improvement in fit.

Our results therefore tell us that there were three major direct influences on whether an individual decided to vote in the referendum in favour of entry into the Common Market. In order of importance these were:

1. (AB) A vote for entry was much more likely if the respondent had voted Tory in February.
2. (AE) A vote for entry was more likely if the respondent was a member of the middle class.
3. (AC) A vote for entry was somewhat more likely if the respondent had had more than the minimal legal schooling.

We can quantify the importance of these statements in a variety of ways. The model provides the following estimated values:

$$\hat{\lambda}_{11}^{AB} = 0.249 \qquad \hat{\lambda}_{11}^{AE} = 0.117 \qquad \hat{\lambda}_{11}^{AC} = 0.071$$

The corresponding estimated odds can be written in the form

$$\exp (2\hat{\lambda}) \text{ to } 1$$

so that we can say that the chances of a vote for entry as opposed to no vote for entry are

1.65 to 1 if respondent voted Tory
1.26 to 1 if respondent belonged to the middle class
1.15 to 1 if respondent had more than minimal schooling

In addition we have

$$\hat{\lambda}_1^A = 0.319$$

which implies a general vote in favour of entry, the odds for a randomly chosen respondent being estimated as

$$\exp (2 \times 0.319) \text{ to } 1$$

that is

1.89 to 1 in favour

If we have information concerning factors B, C, D, and E then our odds change. For example, if we know that a respondent is a minimally schooled, working class, Tory supporter, then the estimated odds on his voting in favour of the referendum are

$$\frac{1.89 \times 1.65}{1.15 \times 1.26} \text{ to } 1$$

that is

$$2.15 \text{ to } 1$$

This compares with the observed values (pooling over D) of $(61 + 34)$ to $(24 + 16)$, which is 2.38 to 1.

Our model has therefore achieved a succinct method of describing an individual's propensity to vote for entry into the Common Market based on knowledge of various characteristics of the individual. The expected frequencies under the model are given in the fourth column of Table 7.6. Notice that the parameter estimates which we have just calculated are identical to those given in Table 7.5 for model 18. This is because the same interactions involving the response variable A were included in the two models.

7.8. MULTISTAGE FACTOR/RESPONSE MODELS

When data are collected which refer to a number of points in time some variables may appear to be simultaneously both factors and responses. They could be considered as responses with the temporally preceding variables being the factors, and as factors with respect to the variables which temporally succeed them. For example, in the referendum data, the February 1975 vote could be regarded as a response to the factors class, schooling, and union membership, and as a factor governing the subsequent decision to vote for entry. Models of this type are discussed by Goodman (1973a, 1973b). The theory is algebraically tedious, though not too difficult, and is omitted here, where we provide the general result for a three-stage situation.

We suppose that we have three sets of variables, $\{P\}$, $\{Q\}$, and $\{R\}$ (each of which may consist of one or more variables), with the first set of variables $\{P\}$ being factors influencing the second set of variables $\{Q\}$, and with both $\{P\}$ and $\{Q\}$ influencing the third set $\{R\}$, so that the set $\{Q\}$ is regarded initially as a set of response variables and subsequently as a set of factor variables.

Write $M(2|1)$ as that model which best described the 'two-way' table of P and Q data (pooled over R, since this has not happened yet!). The model must include the multiway interaction of all the P variables, since these are all factors. Denote the expected frequency in cell (i, j) under $M(2|1)$ by $e_{ij}(2|1)$, and the corresponding observed frequency by f_{ij}. Write $M(3|1, 2)$ as that model best describing the 'two-way' table of the $(P$ plus $Q)$ and R data, which includes the multiway interaction of all the P and Q variables, since these are all factors influencing the R variables. Denote the corresponding expected frequency by $e_{ijk}(3|1, 2)$.

All the models so far tried, including those finally selected ($M(2|1)$ and $M(3|1, 2)$) have been models of the usual log-linear type. We now consider the more complex model M which states that '$M(2|1)$ and $M(3|1, 2)$ are simultaneously true'. This is a different type of model and involves implied conditional probability arguments, but fortunately most of the hard work has been done for us. There are three things that concern us: the goodness of fit of the model, the estimates of the parameters, and the estimated cell frequencies of the model. The first two are easily obtained; the last requires further calculation.

The degrees of freedom of M are equal to the sum of the separate degrees of freedom of $M(2|1)$ and $M(3|1, 2)$, and the value of Y^2 is correspondingly equal to the sum of the individual Y^2 values.

The estimates of the parameters are those obtained from the separate models; thus interactions involving Q variables and P variables with Q variables are estimated from $M(2|1)$, while interactions involving the R variables are estimated from $M(3|1, 2)$. The estimated cell frequencies involve the conditional nature of the model, so that for cell (i, j, k) we calculate

$$e_{ijk}^* = \frac{e_{ijk}(3|1, 2)e_{ij}(2|1)}{f_{ij}}$$

7.9. EXAMPLE OF MULTISTAGE MODEL

We return once again to the referendum data. We have the following sets of variables:

P C, D, E (social background)
Q B (February 1975 Tory identification)
R A (referendum vote)

We first consider the collapsed table of cell frequencies given as Table 7.8. We must consider only models which include the three-factor interaction CDE. Our original saturated model referred to the extended five-variable

Table 7.8. Referendum data pooled over variable A

Cell	Frequency	Cell	Frequency	Cell	Frequency	Cell	Frequency
1111	59	1121	179	1112	39	1122	85
2111	86	2121	85	2112	177	2122	111
1211	17	1221	48	1212	50	1222	85
2211	38	2221	44	2212	249	2222	209

situation, and though it will still provide a useful guide it is easy to fit a new saturated model to the collapsed table. The standardized values of the parameters involving the response B are given in Table 7.9.

Table 7.9. Standardized parameter estimates for the saturated model for Table 7.8 data

Parameter	Standardized value	Parameter	Standardized value
B	−8.96	BCD	−1.49
BC	3.50	BCE	0.70
BD	−7.67	BDE	−0.12
BE	7.61	$BCDE$	0.60

It is apparent from Table 7.9 that the model that is likely to provide a good and satisfactory fit is that defined by $BC/BD/BE/CDE$. This proves to be the case and we shall not reproduce the testing necessary to confirm this statement. This model $M(B|C, D, E)$ has 4 degrees of freedom and a Y^2 value of 4.09, which clearly provides an excellent fit.

We now turn to the five-variable table, regarding variables B, C, D, and E as factors influencing the response A. This is the situation that we considered in Section 7.7, where we found that the most satisfactory model was model 38, $AB/AC/AE/BCDE$, which we could now refer to as model $M(A|B, C, D, E)$.

Our composite model M which states that both model $M(B|C, D, E)$ and model $M(A|B, C, D, E)$ are true, therefore has $(4+12)=16$ degrees of freedom and a Y^2 value of $(4.09+16.48)=20.57$. We can therefore accept M as providing an excellent explanation of the data.

The estimated frequencies under the two separate models can be calculated automatically by the computer, for example $e_{2222}^{BCDE} = 203.67$, using $M(B|C, D, E)$ while $e_{22222}^{ABCDE} = 116.83$, using $M(A|B, C, D, E)$. Since $f_{2222}^{BCDE} = 209$, we calculate the expected frequency under the composite model M as

$$e_{22222}^{*ABCDE} = \frac{116.83 \times 203.67}{209} = 113.85$$

which compares with the observed value of 110. The estimated frequencies for our composite two-stage model are given as the last column in Table 7.6, where they can be seen to be very comparable to those obtained in the previous models.

7.10. SUMMARIZING THE RESULTS USING A PATH DIAGRAM

Since we are now recognizing the ordered nature of the variables it is natural to wish to provide a summary which incorporates this ordering. A convenient method, providing no three-variable interactions are of importance, is provided by using a path diagram.

The path diagram for the referendum data is shown as Figure 7.1. A single arrowed line implies that one variable affects another; for example C, E, and D affect B, while E, C, and B affect A. A doubly arrowed line implies an interrelation between two variables—which is cause and which effect is not stated.

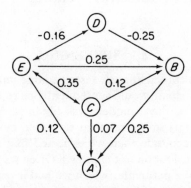

Figure 7.1. Path diagram for referendum data

The figures beside the arrows refer to the λ values calculated from the relevant model. Thus in Section 7.7 we found that (in model $M(A|B, C, D, E)$) $\hat{\lambda}_{11}^{AB}$ was equal to $0.249 \simeq 0.25$, and so this value is attached to the AB line on the graph. The figures for the DE and CE arrows were obtained from an analysis of the collapsed CDE table.

Notice that this method of summary is only relevant to dichotomous situations in which no multifactor interactions are found to be of importance. Note also that Goodman quantifies his arrows somewhat differently.

The precise political/sociological interpretation of the path diagram that we have obtained is left to the reader. The author merely remarks that while union membership D has apparently no direct bearing on referendum vote A it could well have a substantial indirect bearing through the DB and DE arrows.

An alternative method of analysing contingency tables which also leads to path diagrams has been suggested by Davis (1976). His techniques are somewhat similar to those discussed here, but are based on proportions rather than on odds.

CHAPTER 8

Further Techniques for the
Analysis of Multiway Tables

8.1. SCREENING

In the last chapter we conscientiously tested a large number of models, many of which we could anticipate would subsequently be rejected. Our insight into the likely behaviour of these models was obtained from the standardized values of the parameters in the relevant saturated model. If a standardized value was large in magnitude then we expected that that parameter would make a significant contribution to the model. Often we introduced a model to test the importance of a parameter which we had investigated earlier, and in Table 8.1 we pick out some of the comparisons we made in Tables 7.3 and 7.7 concerning the parameter AE; it is easy to see that all our comparisons resulted in very similar assessments of the importance of this parameter.

Table 8.1. The Y^2 contributions of the interaction AE for the referendum data

Models compared	Y^2 values	Y^2 contribution due to AE
1, 3	9.87, 23.46	13.59
18, 21	22.32, 36.74	14.42
32, 34	9.26, 22.74	13.48
38, 40	16.48, 30.96	14.48

Brown (1976) has suggested that approximate bounds for the Y^2 contribution of a parameter can be obtained by obtaining the contributions in two extreme situations. He suggests that, on the one hand, the parameter should be tested when it is the most complex parameter of a simple model and, on the other hand, it should be tested when it is a relatively simple parameter within a complex model. To illustrate the method, consider a four-variable (A, B, C, D) situation, with AB as the parameter under scrutiny. According to Brown's rules, one test, which he calls a test of *marginal association*, compares the simple models AB and A/B, while the second test, termed a test of *partial association*, compares the complex models $AB/AC/AD/BC/BD/CD$ and $AC/AD/BC/BD/CD$.

In the mixed factor/response situation the definitions of the tests of marginal and partial association need adjustment to take account of the fact that the only relevant models are those containing all the factor interactions. Thus if A, B, and C are factors and D is a single response, then we consider only models including the ABC interaction. For example, to test the importance of the interaction ACD we compare the two models ABC/ACD and $ABC/AD/CD$ (marginal association) and the two models $ABC/ABD/ACD/BCD$ and $ABC/ABD/BCD$ (partial association). The results for the factor/response treatment of the referendum data are given in Table 8.2.

Table 8.2. Screening the factor/response referendum data

Parameter	Marginal χ^2 contribution	Partial χ^2 contribution	Parameter	Marginal χ^2 contribution	Partial χ^2 contribution
A	58.4	58.4	ACD	1.0	0.1
AB	105.7	63.8	ACE	3.0	2.4
AC	28.2	6.5	ADE	0.0	0.0
AD	14.2	1.2	$ABCD$	4.5	5.0
AE	52.4	13.7	$ABCE$	0.4	0.6
ABC	0.0	0.1	$ABDE$	0.1	0.1
ABD	1.1	1.3	$ACDE$	0.7	2.5
ABE	1.1	0.9	$ABCDE$	3.1	3.1

Brown refers to the process of calculating the two tests as *screening*, and suggests that scrutiny of the results will result in the classification of the parameters into one of three types. These types are

1. Definitely important (in our example A, AB, AC, AE)
2. Definitely unimportant (ABC, ABD, ABE, ACD, ADE, $ABCE$, $ABDE$)
3. In need of further study (AD, ACE, $ABCD$, $ACDE$, $ABCDE$)

The result of our screening is therefore to concentrate on the parameters classified as type 3, and so far as possible to omit the parameters classified as type 2. The actual classification, of course, is based on the observed χ^2 values and has been done on an *ad hoc* basis, the guiding rule being a comparison of the observed χ^2 contributions with the corresponding χ^2 significance points; when unsure of the status of a parameter it is assigned to type 3 (see especially AD in Table 8.2).

The results in Table 8.2 refer to the factor/response treatment of the referendum data and virtually identical results are obtained for the all factor treatment of the data: this stability will generally be the case.

Screening should be seen as an alternative to fitting the saturated model: either is a sensible preliminary step on the path to a suitable unsaturated model. Screening provides considerably more information than the saturated model, since it gives an idea of the range of importance of the parameters whereas the saturated model provides only a point estimate. This information is gained at the cost of a much greater amount of computer time, since for each parameter the computer has to compare the results of four models. If computer time is of no account then screening is to be preferred, but the saturated model alone provides, as we saw, a very adequate starting point for our analysis.

8.2. THE ANALYSIS OF RESIDUALS

Situations can arise where a single anomalously large (or small) cell frequency can give a misleading impression of the interrelations that exist between the variables. Sometimes such a cell frequency may occur because of a clerical error; at other times it may occur naturally because of the effect of some other variable not previously considered in the model. Whatever the reason it will obviously be of use to have available a simple means of detecting the existence of such an observation, and in general of finding out why a particular model does not provide a good fit to the data.

Our data consist of counts. An anomaly will show up as a *proportionately* large discrepancy between the observed and expected cell frequencies: a difference of 100 would be of no consequence if we were comparing 12,000 and 12,100, but would be of vital significance if we were comparing 12 and 112. Consequently, we need a way of assessing these differences which takes their magnitude into account. Haberman (1973) suggests a number of possible definitions for these residual differences, of which the simplest is

$$r = \frac{f - e}{\sqrt{e}} \qquad (8.1)$$

where r is termed the standardized residual and f and e are respectively the observed and estimated cell frequencies. The distribution of r is approximately normal with mean 0 and variance 1, though we should note that the various cell residuals will inevitably be somewhat correlated with one another. One advantage of the definition (8.1) is that it is conveniently linked to the usual X^2 goodness-of-fit statistic, since

$$X^2 = \sum_{\text{all cells}} r^2 \qquad (8.2)$$

Nelder (1974) cites an alternative definition suggested by Anscombe (1953) which is claimed to be more nearly normally distributed. This is

$$r^* = \frac{3[f^{2/3} - (e - \frac{1}{6})^{2/3}]}{2e^{1/6}} \qquad (8.3)$$

because of the simplicity of (8.1) we shall prefer r in what follows.

As an example we refer to the referendum data of Table 7.6, and in particular to cell $(1, 1, 2, 1, 2)$ where the observed frequency of 21 compares with the expected frequency, under model 18, of 33.8. The corresponding standardized residual is $(21-33.8)/\sqrt{33.8} = -2.2$. This is a fairly extreme value: if we consult tables of the normal distribution we find that less than 3 per cent of randomly chosen observations from the unit normal distribution would be by chance this far (or further) from the mean of 0. However, (a) this was not a randomly chosen observation but rather was the cell with the largest standardized residual and (b) 3 per cent. is about 1 in 33, and we have 32 residuals (one for each cell). Consequently, we should *not* be alarmed by this deviation and can reasonably regard it as a chance deviation from the model.

As well as locating anomalous cell frequencies, the calculation of residuals may also help us to detect patterns in the data which we might otherwise have overlooked. For example, if a variable has several categories, rather than just two, then there may exist some sort of trend across these categories which our model has failed to account for—in which case, of course, we should adjust the model accordingly.

A useful technique employed by Haberman (1973) involves plotting the standardized residuals on graph paper. If the plotting positions are made to correspond to appropriate values from a normal distribution then the plotted points should be approximately on a straight line. A departure from a straight line indicates one or more anomalous observations. The technique was originally introduced by Daniel (1959) to aid the analysis of variance techniques for quantitative data, and some recent improvements in that context have been suggested by Zahn (1975). Applications to frequency data are described by Cox and Lauh (1967) and Fienberg (1969), as well as by Haberman.

8.3. THE MULTIPLICATIVE FORM OF THE LOG-LINEAR MODEL

The models with which we have been concerned in the last three chapters have all been expressed in terms of logarithms; i.e. each model has equated the logarithm of a cell probability to some linear combination of the logarithms of odds or odds ratios (compare equations 5.8). However, as we saw in Section 7.7, when we come to the final interpretation of our selected model it may be easier to interpret our results in terms of odds rather than log odds. In fact any log-linear model can be written quite simply in terms of odds ratios, and Goodman underlines this point by continually switching between the alternative forms of presentation; see especially Goodman (1972a, 1972b, 1973a).

To classify the relation between the two forms we shall consider the following simple situation in which there are three variables A, B, and C each with two or more categories. Reintroducing the notation of Chapter 5 we have p_{ijk} as the unknown theoretical probability for cell (i, j, k) and $v_{ijk} = \log_e (p_{ijk})$, so that the model AB/C can be written in log-linear form as

$$v_{ijk} = \mu + \lambda_i^A + \lambda_j^B + \lambda_k^C + \lambda_{ij}^{AB} \tag{8.4}$$

We now define η, t_i^A, etc., by

$$\mu = \log_e (\eta) \qquad \lambda_i^A = \log_e (t_i^A) \qquad \text{etc.} \tag{8.5}$$

so that we can rewrite (8.4) in the following multiplicative fashion:

$$p_{ijk} = \eta\, t_i^A t_j^B t_k^C t_{ij}^{AB} \tag{8.6}$$

We can interpret this expression most easily by considering the various categories of variable C. Let us suppose that C has K categories, so that $k = 1, 2, \ldots, K$. Then, if a particular category k has greater than average frequency the corresponding t_k^C will be greater than 1, and if less than average then t_k^C will be less than 1 ('average' here is actually the geometric mean, though this need not worry us). The corresponding log parameters, λ_k^C, will correspondingly be positive or negative.

Because of the relation of each category to the geometric mean the individual t's are all subject to the constraints:

$$\prod_i t_i^A = \prod_j t_j^B = \prod_k t_k^C = \prod_i t_{ij}^{AB} = \prod_j t_{ij}^{AB} = 1 \tag{8.7}$$

When there are only two categories for a variable this means that $t_1 t_2 = 1$ and so $t_2 = 1/t_1$. Equivalently, therefore, taking logarithms, $\lambda_2 = -\lambda_1$. In general, with, for example, K categories for variable C, we can interpret the t's in terms of the relative probabilities of the categories of the variable by noticing that every item must belong to some one of the K categories. Since

$$\frac{p_{ijk}}{p_{ijk'}} = \frac{t_k^C}{t_{k'}^C} \tag{8.8}$$

with a little manipulation we can state that the probability that it is category k' of variable C to which an item belongs is

$$\frac{t_{k'}^C}{\sum_{k=1}^{K} t_k^C} \tag{8.9}$$

although when interactions are included in the model the interpretation of this type of statement is less obvious.

Davis (1974) treats the log-linear model solely in multiplicative terms (though with his own notation) and discusses their interpretation at length.

8.4. TABLE ADJUSTMENT—MOSTELLERIZING

Suppose that we take a sample from a population in order to study the interrelation between two variables. The visual appearance of the interrelation will depend to a large extent upon the relative frequencies of the various categories of the variables. The data given in the two halves of Table 8.3 (fictitious data, I hasten to add!) illustrate the point: Table 8.3(a) shows the data collected by a young batchelor member of a survey team, while Table 8.3(b) shows the corresponding data collected by a middle-aged lady member of the team. The data are supposed to investigate the relation, if any, between sex and political allegiance. The two sets of results demonstrate a very marked bias towards females on the part of the young bachelor, and the two tables appear so different that one is tempted to say that they are irreconcilable. This is not the case, as we shall see.

Table 8.3. Relation between sex and political allegiance
(a) collected by young bachelor and (b) by middle-aged lady

	(a)				(b)		
	Conservative	Labour	*Total*		Conservative	Labour	*Total*
Female	220	80	300	Female	60	30	90
Male	30	70	100	Male	20	90	110
Total	250	150	400	*Total*	80	120	200

In our imaginary survey the prime interest centred on the interrelation between sex and political allegiance, so we first concentrate on eliciting this from the data in the tables. What we need to do is to remove all category bias from the table, and it was Mosteller (1968) who first described the method by which this should be done. He gives a number of carefully detailed examples of the process, and further examples are provided by Fienberg (1971) and Smith (1976). The method involves the use of the Deming–Stephan algorithm, which was the basis of the estimation (e.g. ECTA) used in the determination of the parameter values of our various log-linear models. In the previous use the algorithm starts with a table, all of whose entries are unity, and adjusts them until their sums agree with the appropriate observed marginal totals (compare Section 7.1). In the current use the algorithm starts with the observed table of cell frequencies and adjusts these to agree with the marginal totals that we specify. Because the same algorithm is used in the two cases, this latter adjustment, which we shall term *mostellerizing* and others term *standardizing*, can be done by the same computer program used in the production of our earlier results. The result of mostellerizing is shown in Table 8.4, where the total frequency for each category of each variable has been made the same for both data sets. The figures in the body of each table therefore differ only because of the association between the variables sex and political allegiance. If there were no association then each figure would be exactly 50; as it is, it is clear that there is a substantial association between the variables and, furthermore, and most important so far as we are concerned, that this association is the same (given a little random variation) for both sets of data—we can recover useful information from Table 8.3(a) concerning association.

Table 8.4. *The associations between sex and political allegiance, after removal of observer bias*

	(a)				(b)		
	Conservative	Labour	*Total*		Conservative	Labour	*Total*
Female	71.7	28.3	100	Female	75.0	25.0	100
Male	28.3	71.7	100	Male	25.0	75.0	100
Total	100	100	200	*Total*	100	100	200

This is not the end for us, because if we know the true population proportions for the categories of our variables then we can use this information and adjust our tables so that they mirror the population proportions.

Table 8.5. *Table 8.3 after adjustment to the known population sex ratio and known political allegiance*

	(a)				(b)		
	Conservative	Labour	*Total*		Conservative	Labour	*Total*
Female	38.8	12.2	51	Female	40.4	10.6	51
Male	16.2	32.8	49	Male	14.6	34.4	49
Total	55	45	100	*Total*	55	45	100

In Table 8.5 we see the effect of adjusting the results in Table 8.3 so that they coincide with the supposed characteristics of the population (51 per cent. female, 55 per cent. conservative). The procedure for obtaining these results is the same as before—we are simply utilizing different target margins—and once again we find that the interviewers have provided us with very similar results in terms of the composition of the population, despite their individual biases.

Further insight into the mostellerization procedure and into the interpretation of the parameters of log-linear models is provided by fitting saturated models to each of the six tables given in this section; the results are given in Table 8.6. The interaction between sex and political allegiance is quantified by λ^{AB}, and it is evident that mostellerization leaves this unchanged. When the margins are made equal to one another in Table 8.4 the corresponding parameters λ^A and λ^B become 0, as one would expect. When the population values are superimposed in Table 8.5, these are reflected in the values of λ^A and λ^B, but it should be noted that despite the margins being the same in Table 8.5(a) as those in Table 8.5(b), the corresponding values of λ^A (0.11 and 0.12) are not equal, and nor are those of λ^B (-0.03 and -0.04). This is because the associations in the two tables are not identical (0.47 and 0.55), and provides further evidence of the hierarchical implications embodied in the models that we have studied.

Table 8.6. Parameter estimates for the saturated models fitted to Tables 8.3, 8.4, and 8.5

Subtable	λ^A	λ^B	λ^{AB}	Subtable	λ^A	λ^B	λ^{AB}
8.3(a)	0.04	0.53	0.47	8.3(b)	-0.20	0.00	0.55
8.4(a)	0.00	0.00	0.47	8.4(b)	0.00	0.00	0.55
8.5(a)	0.11	-0.03	0.47	8.5(b)	0.12	-0.04	0.55

8.5. ALTERNATIVE METHODS OF TESTING AND ESTIMATION

The methodology of Chapters 5 to 7 has been that advocated at length by Professor Goodman. The method obtains maximum likelihood estimates of the parameters of a log-linear model by an indirect method based on using the Deming–Stephan algorithm to first obtain the corresponding estimates of the cell frequencies for the model under consideration. We have seen that, because of the simplicity of the application of the Deming–Stephan algorithm, it is possible very quickly to try out a large number of alternative models. There are, however, some drawbacks: all the models are log linear and further are of a hierarchical nature. Although the method is simple to use, given the computer program, it is a new method and not all researchers will have the relevant program available. We therefore now look briefly at some other approaches to the analysis of nominal level data. A fuller, but still brief, account of these approaches is given by Bishop, Fienberg, and Holland (1975).

The most appealing of the alternatives is that based on the method of weighted least squares. The principal benefits of this approach are: (a) that the method can be used to construct log-linear models of non-hierarchical form and to construct models of linear form, as well as dealing with the models that we have analysed to date, and (b) that the model uses the standard analysis of variance techniques which are widely available in computer packages and are generally familiar.

We start by considering the situation in which there is a single factor variable with I categories and a single response variable with J categories (though this formulation is solely for descriptive convenience and the approach generalizes to any number of factors and responses). Our interest centres around the variations in the relative probabilities of the J response categories caused by the influences of the factor categories.

To tie in with our existing terminology we denote by p_{ij} the theoretical probability of an observation belonging to the cell (i, j), though this notation conflicts with that used in the literature. We are concerned with the magnitudes of the quantities $\{\pi_{ij}\}$, where

$$\pi_{ij} = \frac{p_{ij}}{\sum_j p_{ij}} \tag{8.10}$$

The corresponding estimates for these conditional probabilities are the observed cell relative frequencies:

$$\hat{\pi}_{ij} = \frac{f_{ij}}{f_{i0}} \tag{8.11}$$

where $f_{i0} = \sum_j f_{ij}$. We need, using the weighted least squares approach, the variances and covariances of the $\{\hat{\pi}_{ij}\}$ which, using standard binomial theory, are seen to be

$$\text{var}\,(\hat{\pi}_{ij}) = \pi_{ij}\frac{(1 - \pi_{ij})}{f_{i0}}$$

$$\text{cov}\,(\hat{\pi}_{ij}, \hat{\pi}_{ik}) = -\frac{\pi_{ij}\pi_{ik}}{f_{i0}} \tag{8.12}$$

$$\text{cov}\,(\hat{\pi}_{ij}, \hat{\pi}_{lk}) = 0 \qquad \text{for } i \neq l$$

It will be noticed that these expressions are given in terms of the unknown quantities $\{\pi_{ij}\}$, and we therefore approximate by replacing the true $\{\pi_{ij}\}$ by the approximate $\{\hat{\pi}_{ij}\}$ in the right-hand sides of equations (8.12). Fortunately this approximation is known to have little effect on the subsequent theory providing that the $\{f_{i0}\}$ are not small.

The next stage in the weighted least squares approach is to formulate functions of the $\{\pi_{ij}\}$ of interest. When $J = 2$ the best choice would seem to be functions such as $g_i = \log(\pi_{i1}/\pi_{i2})$, but for $J > 2$ there are various possibilities. Lehnen and Koch (1974a, 1974b) use functions such as $g_{i1} = \log(\pi_{i1}/\pi_{i2})$ and $g_{i2} = \log[\pi_{i3}/(\pi_{i1} + \pi_{i2})]$. The corresponding observed function values we denote by y_i, y_{i1}, and y_{i2}, so that, for example, $y_i = \log(f_{i1}/f_{i2})$.

The object of the analysis is to explain the observed variation in the y's by a linear function of the unknown λ parameters and to obtain estimates of the latter. In the general case we have $I(J-1)$ g functions and hence $I(J-1)$ observed y values, to be explained by some number, r say, of parameters. In matrix terminology we write the model as

$$g = X\lambda \tag{8.13}$$

where g is the $I(J-1)$ column vector of g functions, λ is the $r \times 1$ column vectors of parameters and X is the $I(J-1) \times r$ design matrix relating the two vectors.

The least squares process provides an estimated value of λ based on the $I(J-1) \times 1$ vector of observations y. Because the $\{\hat{\pi}_{ij}\}$ have the variances and covariances given by equations (8.12) rather than all being uncorrelated with unit variance as in ordinary least squares theory, the form of the least squares estimate is complex; namely

$$\hat{\lambda} = (X'V^{-1}X)^{-1}X'V^{-1}y \tag{8.14}$$

where V is the relevant $I(J-1) \times I(J-1)$ variance–covariance matrix, whose exact form depends on the form of the g functions and includes reciprocals of the observed cell frequencies. The form of the V matrix and further details of the calculations necessary for testing models are given by Grizzle, Starmer, and Koch (1969), Theil (1971), and Bock (1975).

There are various drawbacks to the weighted least squares approach: the estimates obtained are approximate by virtue of the variance approximations, and if there are zero cell frequencies then these have to be replaced by an arbitrary number to avoid problems with the reciprocal of zero. Although a great variety of models can theoretically be investigated using the same basic technique, each model requires a new X matrix and λ vector. Examples of the cumbersome X matrices that arise are seen in the interesting problems considered by Lehnen and Koch (1972, 1974a, 1974b) who analyse data which are incomplete—and which could not easily be treated by the Goodman approach. Knoke (1975) and Goodman (1976) comment on some aspects of the differences embodied in the two approaches.

A further alternative approach is that based on the method of minimum discrimination information estimation, but this in the form proposed by Ku and Kullback (1968) and Ku, Varner, and Kullback (1971) leads to identical estimates to those given by maximum likelihood. A modification of the process was proposed by Ireland, Ku, and Kullback (1969), and this has some advantages in the analysis of symmetrical square contingency tables.

One final comment in this section. It is, of course, always possible to write down the joint likelihood of the observed cell frequencies for a given model and to then use standard numerical function maximization techniques on the likelihood or log likelihood. This approach relies on the accuracy and efficiency of the techniques being used, but can prove helpful with the analysis of the incomplete tables that we study in Chapter 10.

8.6. PSEUDO-BAYES ESTIMATES

In multidimensional tables of counts there are frequently a number of cells with zero cell frequencies, and the presence of these zeros can cause problems in the analysis. We will examine the problems in the order in which the techniques have been discussed, so that we start with the saturated model. If there are zeros present then Goodman has suggested that 0.5 be added to each cell, and indeed by analogy to the familiar binomial continuity correction it is not surprising that the addition of 0.5 to each cell frequency is believed to be a good idea, irrespective of the size of the cell frequencies.

With unsaturated models the presence of individual zero cells is no problem unless there are so many zero cells that they result in fitted zero marginal totals. If these totals refer to factors rather than responses, then a simple solution is to reduce the number of factor categories by omitting those with zero marginal totals; in other cases, the maximum likelihood cell estimates can still be obtained in the usual way, but the parameter estimates and degrees of freedom will need special computation as described in Chapter 10.

The weighted least squares approach to the analysis of tables of counts involves the reciprocal of cell frequencies and thus any zero count constitutes a problem. Also, if a table contains zero then any mostellerization will leave these zeros unchanged since this technique involves successive multiplications of the cell frequencies and yet, as Bishop, Fienberg, and Holland (1975) put it very aptly, 'some zeroes are smaller than others'. As a consequence of these problems considerable work has been done to decide what would be suitable numbers to be added to the cells to make all the cell frequencies positive; this work has centred on the use of pseudo-Bayes estimates. The bulk of the theory appears in the papers by Fienberg and Holland (1970, 1973) and is amplified by Bishop, Fienberg, and Holland (1975).

The basis of the pseudo-Bayes approach is that, without studying the data, we can make an intelligent guess at the underlying structure of the population from which we have obtained our sample. We might anticipate the relative category probabilities for the various variables and the likely interactions; Bishop, Fienberg, and Holland (1975) suggest various situations in which our knowledge could be fairly detailed. If we have no knowledge then it is suggested that the best guess would be that all the cells had equal probability. Whatever form our guess takes the next stage is to express it explicitly as a table of cell probabilities. We will assume that we have a two-variable situation, for the purposes of illustrating the technique, and will denote our guessed probabilities by $\{q_{ij}\}$.

As usual we denote the observed cell frequencies by $\{f_{ij}\}$ and their total by f_{00}. The next stage of the procedure is then to calculate a constant k which in effect quantifies the worth of our guessed population structure in terms of observations. The constant is given by the formula

$$k = f_{00}^2 - \frac{\sum\sum_{ij} f_{ij}^2}{\sum\sum_{ij} (f_{00}q_{ij} - f_{ij})^2} \tag{8.15}$$

This number k represents the number of hypothetical observations to be added to those that we actually possess, and the distribution of k amongst the cells is simple: we add to f_{ij} the quantity kq_{ij}. In this way we obtain a table in which all the cell counts are positive and which combines our actual data with our previous knowledge. Because of the structure of (8.15), the ratio of hypothetical observations k to actual observations y_{00} is small when the observed population structure is unlike that which we hypothesized, and so it is unlikely that we can come to much harm by making a poor guess. On the other hand, k/f_{00} is large if the observed and hypothesized population structures are very similar, and so it is important that the $\{q_{ij}\}$ should be determined without reference to the $\{f_{ij}\}$ to obviate the possible affects of bias.

An excellent layman's account of the method is provided by Smith (1976).

8.7. MIXED MODELS

The flexibility of the log-linear model enables us to approach the analysis of multiway tables with confidence, and provides us with a comprehensive method for analysing and detecting interrelations between variables. It is not the case, however, that a set of observed cell frequencies can always be attributed to some specific log-linear model, for as we saw in Chapter 7 there may be a whole variety of alternative models which furnish plausible explanations of the data. Alternatively, the structure of the cell probabilities may be linear rather than log linear, and with dichotomous variables the differences may be hard to detect (see Knoke, 1975; Goodman, 1976). Finally, the model may be neither wholly additive (linear) nor wholly multiplicative (log linear), in which case none of the techniques discussed will be appropriate. We close this chapter with an example of such a 'mixed' model, which, while illustrating an interesting and important political point, is important to us as an illustration of the need to regard the techniques that we have discussed as techniques only, and not as substitutes for common sense.

Example 8.1. The Australian donkey vote

In Australian federal elections the single transferable vote system is used: voters are asked to rank the candidates in order of preference, and if a voter's first preference candidate is eliminated then his vote is transfered to his second preference candidate, and so on. At each stage in the vote counting it is the candidate with the least votes who is eliminated, and the total votes for the candidates at each stage are recorded so that the breakdown of second preferences corresponding to the eliminated candidate can be deduced.

The candidates' names appear on the ballot paper in alphabetical order, without the names of their parties of affiliation or any other form of information for the voter. It is an offence not to vote in a federal election and there are therefore a number of uninterested voters who find themselves obliged to vote. These voters—'donkey' voters—habitually fulfil their obligation to vote by writing their preference order as 1, 2, . . . down the ballot paper, coinciding with the alphabetic order of the candidates.

Table 8.7. Second preferences of D.L.P. voters in eleven seats in the 1961 Australian federal election

Ballot order: *D.L.P.–Liberal–Labour*

Constituency	1	2	3	4	5	6
D.L.P. second preference Liberal	2754	6020	4858	7928	6633	3207
D.L.P. second preference Labour	524	771	478	660	436	840

Ballot order: *D.L.P.–Labour–Liberal*

Constituency	7	8	9	10	11
D.L.P. second preference Liberal	1649	8661	2126	2517	2339
D.L.P. second preference Labour	1926	4165	2201	2089	2022

The data in Table 8.7 refers to the votes in eleven seats in the 1961 election; in all of the seats the candidate of the Democratic Labour Party (D.L.P.) was at the top of the ballot paper and the other two candidates followed in the order shown in the table. In each case the D.L.P. candidate was eliminated and the figures given refer to the manner in which the second preferences of the D.L.P. supporters split between the other parties. It is easy to see that when the Liberal Party candidate was second on the ballot the Liberal Party gained about 90 per cent. of the D.L.P. votes, but when third the share fell to about 60 per cent. The difference can be attributed entirely to the habits of the donkey voters whose automatic second preference was the second name on the list.

A log-linear model of these data would reveal interactions between all variables. A simple easily interpretable model is as follows. Suppose that a proportion p of the apparent D.L.P. supporters are donkey voters and that of the true D.L.P. supporters a proportion θ support the Liberals. Then for the ballot order D.L.P.–Liberal–Labour the proportion of D.L.P. voters transferring to the Liberal candidate will be $p + (1-p)\theta$, while for the other ballot order the proportion will be just $(1-p)\theta$. It is easy to calculate that p is about 30 per cent. and that θ is about 85 per cent. The model agrees well with the conclusions reached by Mackerras (1970) in a detailed study of the problem from a political viewpoint, from which the above constituency voting figures were abstracted.

CHAPTER 9

Polytomous Variables and Incomplete Tables

9.1. INTERPRETATION OF THE PARAMETERS IN THE CASE OF POLYTOMOUS VARIABLES

Although we developed the theory of log-linear models in Sections 6.2 to 6.5 and 7.1 and 7.2 in completely general terms, our illustrative material was entirely concerned with dichotomous variables. We turn now to the situations where one or more of the variables in our cross-classification has more than two categories; such a variable is described as a *polytomous* variable. The special problems with polytomous situations arise not from the application of the techniques that we have described, which are unaffected by the numbers of categories of the variables, but from the interpretation of the results of our analyses.

Suppose that we have three variables A, B, and C which have respectively I, J, and K categories. As before we denote the frequency of cell (i, j, k) by f_{ijk} and the logarithm of the theoretical probability for that cell by v_{ijk}, so that the model of no interaction between the variables is

$$v_{ijk} = \mu + \lambda_i^A + \lambda_j^B + \lambda_k^C \qquad (9.1)$$

To remove redundancies in the model we constrain the λ's by

$$\sum_i \lambda_i^A = \sum_j \lambda_j^B = \sum_k \lambda_k^C = 0 \qquad (9.2)$$

so that if we know $\lambda_1^C, \lambda_2^C, \ldots, \lambda_{K-1}^C$ then by reason of the constraint we can determine λ_K^C. There are therefore just $(K-1)$ independent λ's relating to C and so we say that there are $(K-1)$ degrees of freedom associated with the main effect of C; this is just what we did when testing for lack of association in Chapter 4.

The same sort of rules apply to interactions; thus the set of AB interactions $\{\lambda_{ij}^{AB}\}$ are subject to the constraints

$$\sum_i \lambda_{ij}^{AB} = \sum_j \lambda_{ij}^{AB} = 0 \qquad (9.3)$$

and hence there are only $(I-1)(J-1)$ independent λ's relating to the AB

102

interaction. Therefore there are $(I-1)(J-1)$ degrees of freedom associated with the AB interaction. Notice that if $I = J = 2$ then there is only a single independent interaction λ, since then

$$\lambda_{11}^{AB} = -\lambda_{12}^{AB} = -\lambda_{21}^{AB} = \lambda_{22}^{AB} \tag{9.4}$$

and it was for this reason that our earlier results with dichotomies were comparatively easy to interpret.

If there is no obvious structure to the various categories of a variable then there is no alternative but to work with the categories directly and to get a complete listing of all the individual λ's in the model. Sometimes, however, there is a structure which we can identify and which enables us to, for example, replace the K λ-type parameters associated with variable C by $(K-1)$ interpretable combinations of these parameters. Example 9.1 includes variables of both these types. The particular case of ordinal variables is discussed at length by Haberman (1974). Ordinal variables occur in two of the three data sets that we analyse in this chapter.

Example 9.1

Lehnen and Koch (1974a) analyse some data relating to law courts in the State of North Carolina, U.S.A. The data consists of three factors: 'race', (black (1) or white (2)), 'county' (Durham (1) or Orange (2)), and 'type of offence' (drunkenness (1), violence (2), property (3), major traffic (4), or speeding (5)), together with the single three-category response 'outcome of case' (not prosecuted (NP), prosecuted and pleads guilty (G), or prosecuted and pleads not guilty (NG)). The data are given in Table 9.1. There is no obvious structure to the polytomous factor 'type of offence', but one does exist for the polytomous response. We shall use the following two orthogonal combinations:

$$\lambda_1 = \lambda_G - \lambda_{NG}$$
$$\lambda_2 = \lambda_G + \lambda_{NG} - 2\lambda_{NP} \tag{9.5}$$

where the subscripts on the right-hand sides of (9.5) refer to the original categories of the response variables. The combination λ_1 is the log odds of a plea of guilty, given that there is a prosecution. The combination λ_2 reflects the odds on there being a prosecution. We will continue with the analysis in Examples 9.3 and 9.8, but a glance at Table 9.1 suggests that the outcomes in Orange County for a black/offence 1 and a white/offence 2 may be exceptions to the general response pattern.

The most frequently occurring polytomous variables are those which are ordinal in nature. Examples include age, attitude on a three- or five-point scale, social class, etc.

Table 9.1. Criminal cases in North Carolina

Black

	Durham					Orange		
Offence	G	NG	NP		Offence	G	NG	NP
1	33	8	4		1	5	10	1
2	10	10	3		2	5	5	5
3	9	8	2		3	11	5	3
4	4	2	1		4	12	6	1
5	32	3	0		5	20	3	2

White

	Durham					Orange		
Offence	G	NG	NP		Offence	G	NG	NP
1	53	2	2		1	14	2	0
2	7	8	1		2	1	5	7
3	10	5	2		3	5	4	0
4	16	3	2		4	13	13	1
5	87	5	3		5	98	16	7

Example 9.2

Williams and Grizzle (1972) use an analysis of variance approach based on ranks to analyse data provided by Bahr (1969), which is given in Table 9.2. In this table it is clear that both the variables 'extent of drinking' and 'number of years in quarters' are essentially ordinal, and so for both variables the natural contrasts (combinations) are $\lambda_3 - \lambda_1$, which measures 'linearity' of trend across the categories of the variable, and $\lambda_3 - 2\lambda_2 + \lambda_1$, which measures

Table 9.2. Drinking habits of subjects living in group quarters

Location	Number of years in quarters	Extent of drinking		
		Light	Moderate	Heavy
Bowery	0	25	21	26
	1–4	21	18	23
	5+	20	19	21
Camp	0	29	27	38
	1–4	16	13	24
	5+	8	11	30
Park Slope	0	44	19	9
	1–4	18	9	4
	5+	6	8	3

departures from linearity. These contrasts are the standard orthogonal polynomial contrasts used in the analysis of variance, and are automatically provided by the ECTA program. A superficial study of the data suggests that there is a relatively high proportion of light drinkers at Park Slope and there is a relatively high proportion of heavy drinkers among those who have lived for five or more years at Camp. We shall complete the analysis in Example 9.4.

9.2. THE SATURATED MODEL AS A GUIDE

Having decided on the form of display (i.e. the contrasts) for each of the variables in the model we are now ready to commence our analysis which, as with dichotomous variables, begins with an examination of the standardized values of the parameter estimates for the saturated model. These are automatically calculated by the computer program as in Chapter 6, but one difference arises in assessing the importance of 'an interaction'. This is easily seen by considering two variables A and B with I and J categories respectively. If no special contrasts are used then there will be a total of IJ individual values subsumed under the heading 'AB interaction', one value corresponding to each of the $\{\lambda_{ij}^{AB}\}$. Various possibilities arise, of which the simplest is that each of the $\{\lambda_{ij}^{AB}\}$ has magnitude less than 2, in which case we can reasonably confidently eliminate this interaction from the model (subject to the usual hierarchial constraints). Alternatively, if just one or two of the $\{\lambda_{ij}^{AB}\}$ lie outside the range -2 to 2, then we may conclude that there is a significant interaction involving these categories. Of course, if one cell is, for example, unusually large then the remaining cells being considered will appear unusually small in comparison to the large cell, and this may result in all the $\{\lambda_{ij}^{AB}\}$ lying outside the range -2 to 2, which would make interpretation difficult until it was realized that it was the single large cell which was creating the problem. We shall see all these situations arising in our examples.

Example 9.3

The criminal charge data in Table 9.1 forms a $2 \times 2 \times 5 \times 3$ table with the first three variables A (race), B (county), and C (offence) being factors and the fourth variable D (outcome) being the single response. The parameter estimates for the two-factor interactions with D and for the important three factor interactions are given in Table 9.3. The variables A and B have just two categories so that, for example, $\lambda_{21}^{AD} = -\lambda_{11}^{AD}$; variable C has five categories so that $\lambda_{11}^{CD} + \lambda_{21}^{CD} + \cdots + \lambda_{51}^{CD} = 0$ (barring round-off errors); variable D has the two categories specified by equations (9.5). The results show little direct interaction between A and D, some between B and D; and considerable interaction between C and D. There are also two three-way interactions

Table 9.3. Some parameter estimates and their standardized values for the criminal charge data of Table 9.1.

Parameter	λ_{11}^{AD}	λ_{12}^{AD}	λ_{11}^{BD}	λ_{12}^{BD}	λ_{11}^{CD}	λ_{12}^{CD}	λ_{21}^{CD}	λ_{22}^{CD}
Estimate	−0.18	−0.20	0.36	0.17	0.53	0.68	−1.21	−1.89
Standardized value	−1.40	−0.51	2.86	0.44	2.07	0.82	−4.35	−3.01

Parameter	λ_{31}^{CD}	λ_{32}^{CD}	λ_{41}^{CD}	λ_{42}^{CD}	λ_{51}^{CD}	λ_{52}^{CD}	λ_{111}^{ACD}	λ_{122}^{BCD}
Estimate	−0.43	−0.04	−0.16	0.16	1.28	1.10	−0.85	1.70
Standardized value	−1.77	−0.06	−0.62	0.21	5.70	1.42	−3.32	2.70

of significance. To help with our interpretation of these interactions we now test some unsaturated models. The model $ABC/ACD/BCD$ fits the data well, as was to be expected from the results in Table 9.3; with 10 degrees of freedom the Y^2 value is 11.17. The model $ABC/AD/BD/CD$ is a poor fit ($Y^2 = 47.21$, 26 d.f.), while the model $ABC/BD/CD$ is very little worse

Table 9.4. Fit of model ABC/BD/CD to criminal charge data

Cell	Count	Estimate	Residual	Cell	Count	Estimate	Residual
1111	33	36.9	−0.6	1232	5	8.0	−1.1
2111	53	46.7	0.9	2232	4	3.8	0.1
1211	5	10.7	−1.7	1142	2	1.6	0.3
2211	14	10.7	1.0	2142	3	4.9	−0.9
1121	10	9.6	0.1	1242	6	7.2	−0.4
2121	7	6.7	0.1	2242	13	10.2	0.9
1221	5	3.6	0.7	1152	3	2.3	0.5
2221	1	3.1	−1.2	2152	5	6.2	−0.5
1131	9	12.0	−0.9	1252	3	3.2	−0.1
2131	10	10.8	−0.2	2252	16	15.4	0.2
1231	11	8.3	0.9	1113	4	1.9	1.5
2231	5	3.9	0.6	2113	2	2.4	−0.3
1141	4	5.0	−0.5	1213	1	1.4	−0.3
2141	16	15.2	0.2	2213	0	1.4	−1.2
1241	12	10.2	0.6	1123	3	4.7	−0.8
2241	13	14.6	−0.4	2123	1	3.3	−1.2
1151	32	31.8	0.0	1223	5	4.3	0.3
2151	87	86.3	0.1	2223	7	3.7	1.7
1251	20	20.4	−0.1	1133	2	1.6	0.3
2251	98	98.5	−0.1	2133	2	1.4	0.5
1112	8	6.2	0.7	1233	3	2.7	0.2
2112	2	7.9	−2.1	2233	0	1.3	−1.1
1212	10	3.9	3.1	1143	1	0.3	1.2
2212	2	3.9	−1.0	2143	2	0.9	1.1
1122	10	8.7	0.4	1243	1	1.6	−0.4
2122	8	6.1	0.8	2243	1	2.2	−0.8
1222	5	7.1	−0.8	1153	0	0.9	−1.0
2222	5	6.2	−0.5	2153	3	2.5	0.3
1132	8	5.4	1.1	1253	2	1.5	0.4
2132	5	4.8	0.1	2253	7	7.1	−0.0

($Y^2 = 49.85$, 28.d.f.). The difference between these last two models ($Y^2 = 2.64$, 2 d.f.) confirms that if ABD is omitted then there is no reason to include AD. We now concentrate on the model $ABC/BD/CD$ for which the cell estimates and standardized residuals are given in Table 9.4.

Remembering that $ABC/BD/CD$ is a poor model and that there were significant three-factor interactions, we concentrate our attention on the standardized residuals, which are approximately normally distributed with mean 0 and variance 1. The two cells with the greatest magnitude residuals are $(1, 2, 1, 2)$ and $(2, 1, 1, 2)$, for which the observed frequencies are respectively much larger and much smaller than our model predicts. These are the cells which give rise to the significant three-way λ components. We shall complete the analysis of this data in Example 9.8.

Example 9.4 (Example 9.2 continued)

We continue our analysis of the drinking data given in Table 9.2. There are two factors, A (years) and B (location), and one response, C (drinking). Variables A and C are ordinal, and for these variables the subscript 1 refers to a linear trend and the subscript 2 to a non-linear trend. The location variable B has three subscripts: (1) Bowery, (2) Camp, and (3) Park Slope. Using the saturated model we obtain the estimates given in Table 9.5 (none of the standardized values of the twelve components of the three-variable interaction exceeds 2 in magnitude).

Table 9.5. Interaction estimates for drinking habits data

Parameter	λ_{11}^{AC}	λ_{12}^{AC}	λ_{21}^{AC}	λ_{22}^{AC}	λ_{11}^{AC}	λ_{12}^{BC}	λ_{21}^{BC}	λ_{22}^{BC}	λ_{31}^{BC}	λ_{32}^{BC}
Estimate	0.16	0.03	−0.04	−0.02	−0.11	0.02	−0.40	0.07	0.52	−0.09
Standardized value	2.00	0.78	−0.79	−0.58	−1.34	0.43	−4.75	1.48	4.66	−1.62

A glance at the standardized values of the parameter estimates reveals three interactions of significance. However, if $\lambda_{31}^{BC} = 0.52$ then $\lambda_{11}^{BC} + \lambda_{21}^{BC} = -0.52$ because of the constraints on the parameters. Since we cannot be sure which of these is genuine and which constrained we describe the results for all three B categories: at the Park Slope location there are far fewer heavy drinkers than light drinkers, whereas at the Camp location the situation is reversed, and at Bowery, also, there are fewer light drinkers than heavy drinkers. The one remaining observation concerns the parameter λ_{11}^{AC} whose positive value implies a significant increase in the amount of drinking with increased time spent in quarters.

For an alternative, though less comprehensive set of conclusions, see the source paper (Williams and Grizzle, (1972).

Example 9.5

For a final example of the use of the saturated model we analyse some data which has been analysed previously by Duncan (1975). We shall discuss Duncan's approach to the analysis of polytomous variables in a subsequent section. The data relate to responses to a question concerning changing the way in which the country (U.S.A.) is run. Respondents chose between stating (1) 'that changes should rarely be made', (2) 'that we should be cautious of making changes', (3) 'we should feel free to make changes', and (4) 'we must constantly make changes'. The respondents also stated their political affiliation: (1) Republican, (2) Democratic, or (3) Independent. The survey was carried out both in 1956 and 1971. The data therefore consist of a $4 \times 3 \times 2$ table, which is given as Table 9.6.

Table 9.6. Duncan's change data

	1956			1971		
Response	Republican	Democrat	Independent	Republican	Democrat	Independent
1	4	9	1	2	11	1
2	94	211	46	85	216	87
3	74	164	28	41	166	80
4	28	47	15	31	116	74

Denoting the response as A, political affiliation as B, and year as C, we find that none of the standardized values of the ABC components exceeds 2 in magnitude. There are three two-way components of significance, namely λ_{41}^{AC}, λ_{43}^{AB}, and λ_{42}^{AB} (while of course $\lambda_{42}^{AC} = -\lambda_{41}^{AC}$ since variable C (year) is a dichotomy). The interesting feature here is that it is the category 4 response (constant change) which is picked out in each case. The parameters translate into the statements that (a) far more respondents were in favour of constant change in 1971 than in 1956 and (b) this was particularly marked for Independents and also, though to a lesser extent, for Democrats. These conclusions are the same as those obtained by Duncan.

9.3. SEPARABLE INCOMPLETE TABLES

We shall return to the analysis of our multivariable tables towards the end of this chapter, but we develop first some ideas concerning a special type of situation which will prove useful subsequently. Our current interest centres on incomplete tables. A table is termed *incomplete* if there are certain cells in the table which are logical impossibilities, and for which we can therefore be certain of obtaining a zero cell frequency.

An example of a situation which gives rise to an incomplete table is the cross-classification of the responses to the following two questions in a sample survey:

Question 1   Are you generally for or against A?
Question 2   Is the reason for your answer to Question 1 because of B_1, B_2, or B_3?

Here we have two variables, A with two categories and B with 3. We could cross-classify the survey results for these two questions in a 2×3 table, but there must be a strong argument for the response B_1 following 'for A' being different (perhaps opposite) to the response B_1 following 'against A'. The solution is to cross-classify these two variables in a 2×6 incomplete table as shown in Table 9.7, where '—' implies that the cell is impossible.

Table 9.7. Example of a separable incomplete table

	For A B_1	For A B_2	For A B_3	Against A B_1	Against A B_2	Against A B_3
For A	·	·	·	—	—	—
Against A	—	—	—	·	·	·

Table 9.7 was a particularly simple example of an incomplete table; it contains two distinct non-overlapping rectangles of possible cells. Any such table which can be divided into a set of non-interconnected complete tables is termed *separable*. A second example of a separable table is given in Table 9.8.

Table 9.8. Another separable table

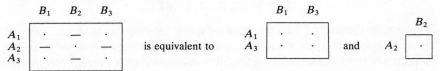

The analysis of separable incomplete tables is easy: one simply separates out the component complete tables and analyses each one in the usual way. The composite model for the incomplete table is then the union of the models for the complete subtables, with the sum of the separate degrees of freedom and the sum of the separate Y^2 values providing the basis for an overall assessment of goodness of fit for the composite model.

9.4. INSEPARABLE INCOMPLETE TABLES

The majority of incomplete tables are not separable; they may arise naturally, as do those illustrated in Tables 9.9 and 9.10, or in the course of an analysis of a complete table when we wish to investigate the importance of a particular cell or group of cells on the model being studied.

Table 9.9. An inseparable triangular table

| | | Total income of household | | | |
		<£3000	£3001–£5000	£5001–£7000	>£7000
Income of head	<£3000	·	·	·	·
of	£3001–£5000	—	·	·	·
household	£5001–£7000	—	—	·	·
	>£7000	—	—	—	·

Table 9.10 An inseparable diagonal-less table

| | | Son's status if different from father's | | |
		1	2	3
Father's	1	—	·	·
status	2	·	—	·
	3	·	·	—

Unsurprisingly, the analysis of inseparable incomplete tables is fraught with difficulties, but these difficulties lie not with estimating the cell frequencies for a particular model but with determining the degrees of freedom for the model and the parameter estimates.

9.5. QUASI-INDEPENDENCE AND OTHER MODELS FOR INCOMPLETE TABLES

The simplest model of interest for a complete table is the model of independence between the variables, which we restate here for the $I \times J$ situation. Suppose that the theoretical probability of a randomly chosen observation belonging to cell (i, j) is p_{ij}, with $p_{i0} = \sum_j p_{ij}$ and $p_{0j} = \sum_i p_{ij}$. The two variables A and B are said to be independent if, for all i and j,

$$p_{ij} = p_{i0}p_{0j} \tag{9.6}$$

Goodman (1968) suggested that the natural extension of this definition to an incomplete table is

$$p_{ij} = p_{i0}p_{0j} \quad \textit{for all cells not necessarily zero} \tag{9.7}$$

The relation (9.7) is said to define the model of *quasi-independence* between the variables A and B.

The cell estimates under the model of quasi-independence are obtained in the same way as for complete tables by means of the Deming–Stephan

algorithm, which in this case starts its iterations with an *incomplete* table of
1's. The computer program ECTA produces the cell estimates without
difficulty.

To determine the degrees of freedom for the model we first calculate the
degrees of freedom for the comparable $I \times J$ complete table and then deduct
the number of impossible cells. This process holds not only for the quasi-
independence model but also for other models applied to incomplete tables.
Thus for Table 9.9 there will be $(3 \times 3 - 6) = 3$ degrees of freedom for the
quasi-independence model and for Table 9.10 there will be $(2 \times 2 - 3) = 1$
degrees of freedom for that model. It is, of course, impossible to fit a model
with less than 0 degrees of freedom, while a model having 0 degrees of
freedom will fit the data exactly.

Fienberg (1970b, 1972) has extended Goodman's results and shows that,
depending on the form of the table, it is possible to fit a variety of other
log-linear models and to obtain parameter estimates. However, it is not
always the case that parameter estimates can be obtained explicitly and the
rules for determining their existence in a general case are complicated (see,
for example, Bishop, Fienberg, and Holland, 1975).

The particular estimates for models suitable for incomplete triangular
tables have been obtained by Bishop and Fienberg (1969) and, in simpler
form, by Altham (1975). The case of the diagonal-less table is analysed in
detail by Wagner (1970).

Example 9.6.

Table 9.11. 1964 and 1966 four-category panel data on British election voting

| | | | 1964 vote | | |
		Conservative	Labour	Liberal	Abstention
	Conservative	157	4	17	9
	Labour	16	159	13	9
1966	Liberal	11	9	51	1
vote	Abstention	18	12	11	15

The data given in Table 9.11 have been abstracted from the panel survey
directed by Butler and Stokes (see, for example, Butler and Stokes, 1975).
These data refer to panel members who remained in the same constituency
during 1964 and 1966 and who had the opportunity to vote for the three
parties shown (and only those three) at both elections.

The large entries (157, 159, 51, 15) along the leading diagonal of the table
demonstrate that the votes of the panel members on the two elections were
not independent. The value of Y^2 for the independence model is 480.4 with
$3 \times 3 = 9$ degrees of freedom.

Table 9.12 shows the expected frequencies for the off-diagonal cells under the hypothesis of quasi-independence. In the present context this hypothesis has the following meaning: if a panel member decided in 1966 not to vote the same way as in 1964 then their 1966 vote was not otherwise affected by their 1964 vote. This sounds odd; what it means is that, for example, renegade Conservatives did not vote Liberal in 1966 to a greater extent than renegade Labour voters or than former Abstainers. It is obvious by comparison of Tables 9.11 and 9.12 that the model fits quite well, the value of Y^2 being 12.3 with $9-4 = 5$ degrees of freedom.

Table 9.12. *Expected frequencies for off-diagonal cells of Table 9.11 under the model of quasi-independence*

		Conservative	1964 vote Labour	Liberal	Abstention
	Conservative	—	9.4	13.4	7.2
	Labour	17.0	—	13.7	7.3
1966	Liberal	10.6	5.9	—	4.5
vote	Abstention	17.4	9.7	13.9	—

9.6. PARTITIONING COMPLETE TABLES—CELL ELIMINATION

In Chapter 3 we showed how the χ^2 goodness-of-fit test could be applied to an $I \times J$ table to test for independence of the two variables and how, by a suitable subdivision and restatement of the table, we could subdivide the degrees of freedom of χ^2 into separate meaningful components. We can do precisely the same kind of trick for multivariable tables and for models other than the simple independence model, by considering the complete table as being a superimposition of a number of incomplete tables and analysing each incomplete table separately. Gail (1972) reanalyses a number of multivariable tables comparing the 'ordinary' model for the complete table with the combined results of quasi-independence models for component incomplete tables. More flexibility still would be allowed by combining other quasi-models into component incomplete tables. In the examples that follow, however, we confine our attention to the elimination of a few isolated cells from the complete table.

Example 9.7.

As a simple example of the procedure we reconsider the fictitious data presented in Table 3.2, which are reproduced in Table 9.13. Our original independence model had a Y^2 value of 15.18 for 6 degrees of freedom and examination of the residuals revealed that the large frequency (13) in cell (1,1) was the principal cause of the lack of fit. We now omit cell (1,1) as shown

Table 9.13. Table 3.2 with cell (1.1) omitted

	B_1	B_2	B_3	B_4
A_1	—	13	12	22
A_2	4	24	28	34
A_3	3	8	15	24

in Table 9.13, and fit the quasi-independence model which gives rise to a Y^2 value of 3.45 with 5 degrees of freedom. We now have a model which fits the data extremely well, and we can state that A and B are independent of one another, with the exception that if B is in category 1 then A is disproportionately likely also to be in category 1. Notice that the difference in Y^2 values between the models of independence and quasi-independence is $15.48-3.45 = 11.73$, associated with 1 degree of freedom, and this is the figure that appears in Table 3.7.

Example 9.8 (Example 9.3 continued)

Returning to our analysis of the criminal charge data given in Table 9.1 we recall that the model $ABC/BD/CD$ was a poor fit to the complete table and that the residuals in Table 9.4 indicated that this was principally due to the cells associated with the plea of guilty to a drunkenness charge. The largest magnitude residual was that for cell $(1, 2, 1, 2)$—a plea of guilty to drunkenness by a black in Orange County—reflecting the unexpectedly high frequency for this cell.

We now consider the incomplete table obtained by omitting cell $(1, 2, 1, 2)$ and analysing the remaining data as if that cell were impossible. The same model $ABC/BD/CD$ applied to the incomplete table now fits moderately well ($Y^2 = 35.60$, 27 d.f.), and the lack of fit of the cell $(1, 2, 1, 2)$ is quantified by the reduction in Y^2 (14.25, 1 d.f.). After refitting the model we now re-examine the residuals and find that the largest residual is that of cell $(1, 1, 1, 2)$—not $(2, 1, 1, 2)$ as might have been expected from the original table of residuals (Table 9.4).

Our next stage is therefore to consider a new incomplete table with both cell $(1, 2, 1, 2)$ and cell $(1, 1, 1, 2)$ omitted. The same model now has a Y^2 value of 30.28 with 26 degrees of freedom and therefore provides quite a good fit. However, the reduction in the Y^2 value of 5.32 is not very great (given that we are deliberately trying to make it large) and does not therefore warrant our treating this cell as a special case.

From the logarithms of the cell estimates it is possible to calculate the parameter estimates for the model. These estimates are unique in this case— the problems with lack of identifiability usually arise only with relatively large numbers of missing cells. The parameters of interest and their estimated values are given in Table 9.14, without the usual standardized values. The latter are difficult to calculate for incomplete tables, but a good idea of their

Table 9.14. *Parameter estimates for the Model ABC/BD/CD with the cell (1, 2, 1, 2) omitted*

Parameter	λ_1^D	λ_2^D	λ_{11}^{BD}	λ_{12}^{BD}	λ_{11}^{CD}	λ_{12}^{CD}	λ_{21}^{CD}
Estimate	1.00	2.91	0.25	0.60	0.94	0.11	−1.26

Parameter	λ_{22}^{CD}	λ_{31}^{CD}	λ_{32}^{CD}	λ_{41}^{CD}	λ_{42}^{CD}	λ_{51}^{CD}	λ_{52}^{CD}
Estimate	−2.07	−0.57	−0.16	−0.31	1.08	1.20	1.04

probable sizes can be gained by a comparison of Tables 9.14 and 9.3. For the most part, the estimates in the two tables are similar, the differences being due to the differences between the models and the omission for the latter table of cell $(1, 2, 1, 2)$. It would seem that the significant λ's are λ_{51}^{CD}, λ_{21}^{CD}, λ_{11}^{CD}, λ_{22}^{CD} and λ_{11}^{BD} (in descending importance), and we can therefore summarize our conclusions as follows:

(a) *Race*. Race has no significant effect on the outcome of a case (λ^{AD}), though see (d) below.

(b) *Prosecuted cases*. The overall proportion of prosecuted cases which elicit a plea of guilty is estimated by the model to be $\exp(2\lambda_1^D)/\{1 + \exp(2\lambda_1^D)\}$, which turns out to be 0.88.

There are significant variations about the overall proportion due to the type of offence. The odds in favour of a plea of guilty are much greater for speeding offences (λ_{51}^{CD}) and are also greater for drunkenness offences (λ_{11}^{CD}), whereas for violence offences the odds favour a plea of not guilty (since $\lambda_{21}^{CD} + \lambda_1^D < 0$).

Pleas of guilty are relatively more frequent in Durham County than in Orange County (λ_{11}^{BD}).

(c) *Cases not prosecuted*. The majority of cases result in prosecution (λ_2^D). The slightly greater proportion of cases not prosecuted in Orange County is of doubtful significance (λ_{12}^{BD}). There is a smaller proportion of prosecutions for the offence of violence (λ_{22}^{CD}) than for other types of offence.

(d) *Black drunkenness offences in Orange County*. Notwithstanding the previous general comments, there is in Orange County an anomalously large numbers of pleas of not guilty by blacks to the charge of drunkenness. This is not totally explained by the previously noted general trends.

Our conclusions mirror those obtained by Lehnen and Koch (1974a). For a brief discussion of their approach to the analysis of this data see Section 9.7.

9.7. ALTERNATIVE APPROACHES TO THE ANALYSIS OF COMPLETE TABLES

The vast bulk of the published literature confines itself to dichotomous variables and scant attention has been paid to polytomies, with the result that well-ordered approaches to dealing with them have not yet been thought out. The approach outlined in Sections 9.2 and 9.6 reflects the author's attitude to the problem. Two alternative approaches are suggested by Lehnen and Koch (1974a) and Duncan (1975).

Lehnen and Koch use the weighted least squares approach of Grizzle, Starmer, and Koch (1969), which was outlined in Section 8.5. With this approach it is not necessary to fit, for example, all $(I-1) \times (J-1)$ of the AB interaction components, but only those judged to be of relevance. Thus where we, in Example 9.8, stopped at a table of parameter estimates and drew conclusions based on these, Lehnen and Koch would go on to verify the importance of the individual interaction components by comparing the goodness of fit of models in the usual way. Without using weighted least squares this is also possible via direct function maximization as noted in Section 8.5.

Using the weighted least squares approach it is also possible to analyse different category comparisons to those available for the indirect Goodman approach. This is most easily seen by example. In Example 9.1 we formulated in equations (9.5) two comparisons of the outcome categories, and, if we write p_1, p_2, p_G, p_{NG}, and p_{NP} for the probabilities corresponding to the log probabilities shown, then we find on antilogging both sides that we have the statements

$$p_1 = \frac{p_G}{p_{NG}} \tag{9.8}$$

and

$$p_2 = \frac{p_G p_{NG}}{(p_{NP})^2} \tag{9.9}$$

Although the right-hand side of (9.8) is a simple odds ratio, the right-hand side of (9.9) is not easily interpreted. Lehnen and Koch, however, are able to work with two easily interpretable ratios p_G/p_{NG} (our p_1) and $p_{NP}/(p_G + p_{NG})$, the latter being the direct odds ratio for a case being not prosecuted as opposed to its being prosecuted.

Although Lehnen and Koch's method can lead to a naturally expressed model for a set of multivariable data, there will not always be such a natural set of response comparisons available, and it is reassuring to note the broad correspondence of the conclusions at the end of Example 9.8 with those obtained by Lehnen and Koch in their own analysis of the Table 9.1 data.

A very different approach is suggested by Duncan (1975) which utilizes the idea of dummy variables to get around the necessity of fitting, for example, all $(I-1)(J-1)$ of the AB interaction terms as mentioned three paragraphs earlier. Using the dummy variable notion, a variable with, for example, three categories is replaced by three dichotomous variables as shown in Table 9.15, for the location variable of Example 9.2. The single three-category variable is replaced by an eight-cell three-variable array, in which five of the cells are logically impossible. The analysis that follows this redefinition of the data is that for incomplete tables, and can be dealt with by the usual methods.

Table 9.15. Representation of a polytomous variable by means of dummy dichotomous variables

Polytomous variable	Location (Bowery, Camp, Park Slope)
Dichotomous variables	X_1 (Bowery, not Bowery)
	X_2 (Camp, not Camp)
	X_3 (Park Slope, not Park Slope)
Possible configurations	$[X_1(1), X_2(2), X_3(2)]$
(1 refers to first level,	$[X_1(2), X_2(1), X_3(2)]$
2 to second level)	$[X_1(2), X_2(2), X_3(1)]$

This approach has the advantage of utilizing the simple Goodman (ECTA) program, although parameter estimates and their standard errors are not easily obtained. Its major disadvantage is that even quite simple problems can become embedded in very large tables. For example, a 2^{10} table is needed for the criminal data in Table 9.1 and a 2^9 table for the drinking data of Table 9.2. The data in Table 9.6 required a 2^8 table and it is reassuring to note that our conclusions in Example 9.5 mirrored those obtained by Duncan using his technique.

9.8. PARTIALLY CATEGORIZED TABLES

A frequent problem familiar to all who handle raw data is the missing observation: either a particular individual fails to answer a relevant questionnaire, or some data is mislaid, or information on a particular variable is unobtainable. The standard practice of the analyst has been a despairing sigh and a reduction of the overall size of the data set. If only a few observations are missing this is unlikely to be serious, but in a multivariable analysis a few missing observations on each variable may amount to a great many missing observations altogether.

Recent work has been done which shows how the partial information available can be combined with the data for which complete information is available to provide improved parameter estimates (Chen and Fienberg, 1974; Hocking and Oxspring, 1974), and Chen and Fienberg (1976) have developed their work to include the testing of various log-linear models. Similar work, based on the weighted least squares approach has been done by Koch, Imrey, and Reinfurt (1972), who provide a number of worked examples.

Unfortunately, the theory of either approach is complex and depends on the form of the missing data, and the interested reader is therefore referred to the papers cited.

CHAPTER 10

Symmetry, Panel Data, and Models of Change

10.1. INTRODUCTION

This chapter deals with the particular type of cross-classification in which each variable has the same number of categories and in which the category definitions are the same for each variable.

There are two principal sources of this type of data: from matched pairs and from panel studies. Classic examples of the types are as follows. Variable A is the social class of a father (husband) and variable B is the social class of a son (wife). Variable A is the political affiliation of a person at a particular point in time and variable B is the same person's political affiliation at a subsequent point in time.

Because of the link between the variable categories, we can postulate models of equality between cells or marginal totals on either side of the leading diagonal of the table. The cells on the leading diagonal represent counts which can be characterized as showing stability or lack of change, and for the most part we shall be concerned with the off-diagonal cells.

10.2. SYMMETRY

A two-dimensional table, with variables A and B each having I categories, is said to be symmetric if

$$p_{ij} = p_{ji} \qquad \text{for all } i, j = 1, 2, \ldots, I \qquad (10.1)$$

where p_{ij} is the theoretical probability of an observation belonging to cell (i, j). The table is symmetric about its leading diagonal.

With more than two variables the concept of symmetry is less easy to specify; e.g. for the three-variable case we need

$$p_{ijk} = p_{ikj} = p_{jik} = p_{jki} = p_{kij} = p_{kji} \qquad (10.2)$$

Since all the information about p_{ij} (or p_{ji}) is contained in the cell frequencies f_{ij} and f_{ji}, it is easy to see that, if the symmetry hypothesis is correct, then the ideal table would have the frequencies in cells (i, j) and (j, i) equal to one

another. In other words, under the model (10.1), the expected cell frequency
for cell (i, j) is

$$e_{ij} = \frac{f_{ij} + f_{ji}}{2} \tag{10.3}$$

It follows from our usual definition of the Y^2 goodness-of-fit criterion that
the test of goodness of fit of the symmetry model (10.1) is provided by
calculating the value of

$$Y_S^2 = 2 \sum_{i \neq j} \sum f_{ij} \log_e \left(\frac{2f_{ij}}{f_{ij} + f_{ji}} \right) \tag{10.4}$$

which has $I(I-1)/2$ degrees of freedom, since this is the number of off-
diagonal pairs of cells.

Example 10.1

The data in Table 10.1, taken from Upton (1977), refer to the voting transitions between 1966 and 1970 of a subset of the members of a panel study
conducted by Butler and Stokes who discuss their findings in Butler and
Stokes (1975). The particular subset to which the data refer are those panel
members who remained, throughout the period 1964 to 1970, in a constituency contested by the Conservative, Labour, and Liberal parties alone. The
table has symmetric classifications, these being the reported votes for the
three parties, together with a reported abstention. For a discussion of the
problems with reports of abstentions see Upton (1977).

Table 10.1. Voting behaviour in 1966 and 1970

		1970 reported vote			
		Conservative	Labour	Liberal	Abstention
1966 reported vote	Conservative	68	1	1	7
	Labour	12	60	5	10
	Liberal	12	3	13	2
	Abstention	8	2	3	6

The symmetry hypothesis may be interpreted as stating that, for example, it
is as likely for a 1966 Conservative to vote for Labour in 1970 as for the
reverse to occur. Common sense tells us that only if there has been no general
'swing' between the parties can we expect this to be true. There is a clear
indication from the table of a swing to the Conservatives in 1970, and this is
reflected in the value of Y_S^2, which is 27.61, which exceeds the upper 0.02 per
cent point of the χ_6^2 distribution. We can reject the hypothesis of symmetry.

10.3. MARGINAL HOMOGENEITY AND QUASI-SYMMETRY

The model of symmetry specified by (10.1) or (10.2) is a very restrictive one: a less restrictive proposition would be that the corresponding marginal probabilities were equal, without demanding complete correspondence of individual cells. For two variables this requires

$$p_{i0} = p_{0i} \qquad \text{for } i = 1, 2, \ldots, I \qquad (10.5)$$

where $p_{i0} = \sum_b p_{ib}$, $p_{0i} = \sum_a p_{ai}$. This model (10.5) is known as the model of *marginal homogeneity*.

Although the model (10.5) is simply stated and easily comprehended it is not easily tested! The reason is that the marginal totals are all interrelated by the probabilities in the body of the table, and we cannot simply compare their sizes directly, but must take into account all the cell frequencies. The direct test of marginal homogeneity requires a complicated sequence of iterations, and we omit it. We give a related test subsequently.

It is easy to see that if a table is symmetric then its margins are homogeneous (algebraically we sum the model 10.1 over two variables and arrive at the model 10.5), but the reverse is not necessarily true except for the 2×2 table. This suggests seeking that 'certain something' which, when added to marginal homogeneity, ensures symmetry. This missing link turns out to be most easily comprehended in log-linear terms. We call our variables A and B and write $v_{ij} = \log_e (p_{ij})$. The following model is termed the model of *quasi-symmetry*:

$$v_{ij} = \mu + \lambda_i^A + \lambda_j^B + \lambda_{ij}^{AB} \qquad i, j = 1, 2, \ldots, I$$

$$\text{subject to } \sum_i \lambda_{\cdot i}^A = \sum_j \lambda_j^B = \sum_i \lambda_{ij}^{AB} = 0 \qquad (10.6)$$

$$\textit{and } \text{to} \qquad \lambda_{ij}^{AB} = \lambda_{ji}^{AB} \qquad \text{for all } i, j$$

It is, of course, the final constraint $\lambda_{ij}^{AB} = \lambda_{ji}^{AB}$ which makes the model special. If both (10.6) and (10.5) are true then automatically so is (10.1).

To fit the model (10.6) we seek agreement, as is usual, between the appropriate observed and expected marginal totals. In this case this implies a need for

$$e_{i0} = f_{i0}$$
$$e_{0j} = f_{0j}$$

and   (10.7)

$$e_{ij} + e_{ji} = f_{ij} + f_{ji}$$

Fitting the third of these constraints is not completely straightforward, but Bishop, Fienberg, and Holland (1975) suggest the following neat solution, which enables us to use a standard computer program. The rules are as follows:

1. Transform the two-dimensional $I \times I$ table into a three-dimensional $I \times I \times 2$ table by writing out the table twice, on the second occasion with the cells on either side of the leading diagonal in reversed positions. Thus we have

$$f_{ij1} = f_{ij}$$

$$f_{ij2} = f_{ji} \tag{10.8}$$

2. Fit the model $AB/AC/BC$, i.e. the model of no three-variable interaction.
3. The estimated cell frequencies for the two categories of C will be identical, subject to the reversal of the second layer, and are the estimates for the quasi-symmetry model for the original table.
4. Because in the three-variable case all the frequencies appear twice, the calculated value of Y^2 (Y_Q^2) should be halved. The degrees of freedom can be deduced from the constraints in (10.6) to be $(I-1)(I-2)/2$.

Since the addition of marginal homogeneity to quasi-symmetry results in complete symmetry, and because of the additivity of Y^2 values, we can use the calculated values of Y_S^2 and Y_Q^2 to provide a conditional test of marginal homogeneity, given the assumption of quasi-symmetry. This is simply $Y_{M|Q}^2 = Y_S^2 - Y_Q^2$ and has $[I(I-1)/2 - (I-1)(I-2)/2] = (I-1)$ degrees of freedom.

Example 10.2 (Example 10.1 continued)

For the data of Table 10.1, the hypothesis of marginal homogeneity states specifically that there has been no change in the proportions of the panel voting for the various parties or abstaining. We first fit the model of quasi-symmetry, writing Table 10.1 in the three-dimensional form shown in Table 10.2.

As is evident from Table 10.2, the model of quasi-symmetry provides a satisfactory fit ($Y_Q^2 = 4.20$, 3 d.f.). This implies that there is symmetry in the table after allowing for the disparity in the marginal frequencies. This disparity is manifest when we consider the conditional test of marginal homogeneity, since we find that $Y_{M|Q}^2 = 23.41$ with just 3 degrees of freedom.

Table 10.2. Table 10.1 arranged for fitting the quasi-symmetry model, with the fitted values shown below the observed values

68	1	1	7
68.0	1.3	2.3	5.4
12	60	5	10
11.7	60.0	5.3	10.0
12	3	13	2
10.7	2.7	13.0	3.6
8	2	3	6
9.6	2.0	1.4	6.0

68	12	12	8
68.0	11.7	10.7	9.6
1	60	3	2
1.3	60.0	2.7	2.0
1	5	13	3
2.3	5.3	13.0	1.4
7	10	2	6
5.4	10.0	3.6	6.0

10.4. SYMMETRY FOR HIGHER-DIMENSIONAL TABLES

In the last two sections we have been concerned with the relatively simple two-way table. When the cross-classification involves three or more variables the analysis rapidly becomes very complicated. For example, to specify the model of symmetry for a three-way cross-classification, with p_{ijk} as the probability of an observation belonging to cell (i, j, k), we need

$$p_{ijk} = p_{ikj} = p_{jik} = p_{jki} = p_{kij} = p_{kji} \qquad (10.9)$$

for all i, j, and k. This model turns out to have $I(I-1)(5I+2)/6$ degrees of freedom, and is not easy to test. For a complete account of the models of symmetry, quasi-symmetry and marginal homogeneity in these situations, see Bishop, Fienberg, and Holland (1975).

10.5. PANEL STUDIES

As was mentioned in the introduction to this chapter, symmetric tables can arise in a wide variety of situations—one much analysed set of data relates to the cross-classification of the degree of distant vision of women employed in Royal Ordnance factories in Britain (right-eye vision and left-eye vision being the variables)—but the most frequently occurring source of symmetric tables arises from panel studies such as that referred to in Example 10.1.

The essential characteristic of a panel study is that the views and opinions, etc., of the members of the panel are noted at a series of points in time. If the questions asked differ on each occasion then an appropriate analysis would follow the procedure for the multistage models described in Section 7.8. Generally, however, the particular interest in these 'follow-up' studies is to see how the panel member's responses to the *same* question change with time. Typically, in the comparatively short time period that elapses between interviews, the responses of the majority of the panel members remain unaltered, and thus the bulk of the observations in a two-variable (two time periods) situation is centred along the leading diagonal. We have already seen a typical example: 147 of the 213 panel members in Table 10.1 reported the same votes in the two elections (69 per cent).

Because of this strong interdependence between the categories of the variables, the standard log-linear models of Chapter 7 are inappropriate since they would reveal the known diagonal interdependence without casting any light on the interrelations (if any) demonstrated by the off-diagonal cell frequencies. The models of symmetry and quasi-symmetry represent an alternative type of approach which may lead to the discovery of some interesting aspects of the data. A further approach is to formulate specific models corresponding to simple concrete explanations of the data and to test their merits. We now discuss models of this type.

10.6. THE MOVER–STAYER MODEL

One of the earliest specialized models for panel data was the mover–stayer model introduced by Blumen, Kogan, and McCarthy (1955) in their analysis of data relating to the types of occupation of panel members at two points in time.

The essence of the model is to suppose that the panel members consist of two basic types, movers and stayers. Stayers are supposed never to change their response category, while movers change their response category from one time period to the next without reference to their previous history of responses. If we were able to isolate the movers from the stayers then we would find that for the stayers all the cells off the leading diagonal were zero, while for the movers the frequencies of the cells, including those on the leading diagonal, would exhibit complete independence.

Unfortunately our panel members do not identify themselves as being movers or stayers; however, we can be certain that all the cells off the leading diagonal contain only movers, and we therefore concentrate on these cells alone. According to the model the movers exhibit independence, and consequently the off-diagonal cells should exhibit quasi-independence. Our analysis therefore consists of fitting the quasi-independence model (9.7) to these cells, and using the fitted cell estimates to determine the parameters in the quasi-independence model from the relations typified by

$$\log (e_{ij}) = \hat{\mu} + \hat{\lambda}_i^A + \hat{\lambda}_j^B \tag{10.10}$$

The observed frequency in the on-diagonal cell (i, i), f_{ii}, comprises an estimated number of movers $\hat{m}_{ii}$ and stayers $\hat{s}_{ii}$. From equation (10.10) we have

$$\log (\hat{m}_{ii}) = \hat{\mu} + \hat{\lambda}_i^A + \hat{\lambda}_i^B \tag{10.11}$$

and hence the best estimate of the number of stayers is given by

$$\hat{s}_{ii} = f_{ii} - \hat{m}_{ii} \tag{10.12}$$

We obtain estimates of the proportions of movers in the I categories by calculating, for example,

$$\hat{p}_k^A = \frac{\exp(\hat{\lambda}_k^A)}{\sum_{i=1}^I \exp(\hat{\lambda}_i^A)} \qquad (10.13)$$

where $\hat{p}_k^A$ represents the proportion in category k at the first time period.

Example 10.3 (Example 9.6 continued)

In Example 9.6 we fitted the quasi-independence model to the off-diagonal cells of Table 9.11, obtaining the expected frequencies shown in Table 9.12. This is the procedure used for the mover–stayer model; this model was found to fit the data quite well, since the Y^2 value was 12.3 with 5 degrees of freedom.

Comparing the logarithms of the expected cell frequencies and using equation (10.10), it is easy to deduce the following estimated values of the parameters:

$$\hat{\mu} = 2.305 \qquad \hat{\lambda}_1^A = 0.415 \qquad \hat{\lambda}_2^A = -0.167$$

$$\hat{\lambda}_3^A = 0.189 \qquad \hat{\lambda}_4^A = -0.436 \qquad \hat{\lambda}_1^B = 0.103$$

$$\hat{\lambda}_2^B = 0.118 \qquad \hat{\lambda}_3^B = -0.359 \qquad \hat{\lambda}_4^B = 0.137 \qquad (10.14)$$

Where the index A refers to the 1964 vote and the index B to the 1966 vote.

From the estimated values in (10.14) we can deduce, using equation (10.11), that

$$\hat{m}_{11} = 16.8 \qquad \hat{m}_{22} = 9.5 \qquad \hat{m}_{33} = 8.5 \qquad \hat{m}_{44} = 7.4 \qquad (10.15)$$

and hence that

$$\hat{s}_{11} = 140.2 \qquad \hat{s}_{22} = 149.5 \qquad \hat{s}_{33} = 42.5 \qquad \hat{s}_{44} = 7.6 \qquad (10.16)$$

According to the model, therefore, about 340 of the 512 panel members (66 per cent) were stayers. Furthermore, using equation (10.13) we see that

$$\hat{p}_{CON}^{1964} = \frac{\exp(0.415)}{\sum_{i=1}^4 \exp(\hat{\lambda}_i^A)}$$

$$= 0.36$$

and the full results are summarized in Table 10.3.

10.7. FAILURE OF THE MOVER–STAYER MODEL

It cannot be expected that, in the social sciences, any mathematical laws can be laid down relating variables to one another—all our models of the last five

Table 10.3. Estimated numbers of stayers and estimated proportions of movers for the data of Table 9.11

Number of stayers				Proportions of movers							
				1964				1966			
Con.	Lab.	Lib.	Ab.	Con.	Lab.	Lib.	Ab.	Con.	Lab.	Lib.	Ab.
140.2	149.5	42.5	7.6	0.36	0.20	0.29	0.15	0.27	0.28	0.17	0.28

chapters have been essentially no better than mathematical simplifications which appear to provide possible explanations of the data. The mover–stayer model is no more of a failure than any of the other models; it has been singled out here because it is comparatively easy to see that, when more data become available, an apparently excellent model can be revealed to have given nonsensical answers. The example that follows should serve as a warning to the data analyst that he or she should not believe too implicitly in his or her own 'pet' model.

Example 10.4

The data (Table 10.4) that we consider is again taken from Upton (1977), being the three-interview counterpart of Table 10.1.

Table 10.4. Voting behaviour 1964, 1966, and 1970

		1964 Conservative						1964 Labour			
		1970						1970			
		Con.	Lab.	Lib.	Ab.			Con.	Lab.	Lib.	Ab.
1966	Con.	57	0	1	5	1966	Con.	2	1	0	0
	Lab.	4	2	0	0		Lab.	7	52	3	10
	Lib.	1	0	0	1		Lib.	1	0	1	1
	Ab.	5	0	0	0		Ab.	1	0	0	3

		1964 Liberal						1964 Abstention			
		1970						1970			
		Con.	Lab.	Lib.	Ab.			Con.	Lab.	Lib.	Ab.
1966	Con.	8	0	0	0	1966	Con.	1	0	0	2
	Lab.	1	5	2	0		Lab.	0	1	0	0
	Lib.	10	3	12	0		Lib.	0	0	0	0
	Ab.	0	1	3	1		Ab.	2	1	0	2

Table 10.4 is a $4 \times 4 \times 4$ three-way table. If we collapse this table over the 1964 categories we obtain Table 10.1; if we collapse it over the 1970 categories we obtain Table 10.5.

Table 10.5. Voting behaviour 1964 and 1966

		1964 reported vote			
		Con.	Lab.	Lib.	Ab.
1966	Con.	63	3	8	3
reported	Lab.	6	72	8	1
vote	Lib.	2	3	25	0
	Ab.	5	4	5	5

We now apply the mover–stayer model separately to Tables 10.5, 10.1, and 10.4 and, using the methods described previously, obtain the results summarized in Table 10.6. The crucial point to be observed in Table 10.6 is that while the model for both two-way classifications provides excellent explanations of the data, the estimates of the stayer numbers (particularly Liberals) differ greatly, so that when the model is applied to the full three-wave data in Table 10.4 the result is a very poor fit.

10.8. SOME SPECIALIZED LOG-LINEAR MODELS

Goodman (1972c) considered a number of specialized models, many of which are particularly relevant to the analysis of square $(I \times I)$ tables. We shall briefly consider two of his models, and it will be easier to understand the motivation behind the models if we relate them to a particular situation. Suppose that the two variables that we consider are the social status of panel members at two points in time. Social status is recorded on a five-point scale on each occasion.

Consider two panel members, one whose status has changed from level 4 to level 3, and another whose status has changed from level 3 to level 2. If the differences between the various levels of social status are equally large, then the change for both panel members has been of equal importance. Both the cells, (4, 3) and (3, 2), lie on the same diagonal of the two-way table, and this suggests incorporating a 'diagonal effect' into the model. An appropriate model is the following:

$$v_{ij} = \mu + \lambda_i^A + \lambda_j^B + \lambda_k^D \tag{10.17}$$

where $k = i - j$ and λ_k^D is the parameter associated with the kth of the $(2I - 1)$ diagonals in the two-way table. There are in all $(2I - 3)$ distinct λ_k^D parameters, one for each of the diagonals of length greater than 1, and thus there are $I^2 - 1 - (I - 1) - (I - 1) - (2I - 3) = (I - 2)^2$ degrees of freedom for this model.

Table 10.6. *Mover–stayer estimates of stayer numbers and mover proportions for Tables 10.5, 10.1, and 10.4*

Table	Numbers of stayers				Proportions of movers			
						1964		
	Con.	Lab.	Lib.	Ab.	Con.	Lab.	Lib.	Ab.
10.5	56.9	67.5	21.9	3.7	0.20	0.36	0.23	0.21
10.1	60.0	56.7	10.3	0.8	—	—	—	—
10.4	54.6	49.9	11.2	1.7	0.22	0.34	0.36	0.08

Table	Proportions of movers								Fit of model	
	1966				1970				Degrees	
	Con.	Lab.	Lib.	Ab.	Con.	Lab.	Lib.	Ab.	of freedom	Y^2
10.5	0.47	0.11	0.14	0.28	—	—	—	—	5	3.6
10.1	0.30	0.23	0.38	0.08	0.32	0.31	0.13	0.24	5	6.5
10.4	0.23	0.39	0.20	0.18	0.48	0.17	0.11	0.24	50	122.0

In another context we may be considering the political allegiance of panel members at two points in time. The categories of the two classificatory variables refer to the various political parties: since some parties are ideologically far apart while others are very similar, a change from affiliation to party 4 to affiliation to party 3 may be of very different importance to a change from party 3 to party 2, in which case the diagonal model will be somewhat inappropriate. Instead we introduce the parameter λ_k^S which we associate with the distance between category k and category $k+1$, thereby arriving at the following 'crossings' model:

$$v_{ij} = \begin{cases} \mu + \lambda_i^A + \lambda_j^B + \sum_{k=i}^{j-1} \lambda_k^S & i<j \\[2mm] \mu + \lambda_i^A + \lambda_j^B + \sum_{k=j}^{i-1} \lambda_k^S & i>j \\[2mm] \mu + \lambda_i^A + \lambda_i^B & i=j \end{cases} \qquad (10.18)$$

There are, in all, $I-1$ of the λ_k^S parameters and thus the model has $I^2-1-3(I-1)=(I-1)(I-2)$ degrees of freedom.

Goodman also studies a large number of other models which combine the crossings and diagonal elements for various parts of the two-way table. In Example 10.5 we illustrate the application of this type of approach to some Swedish voting data.

Example 10.5

The data given in Table 10.7 refer to the votes of 1651 members of a panel drawn at random from the Swedish electorate. The panel members were interviewed immediately after the elections of 1964, 1968, and 1970. The data given refer to the panel members who voted on each occasion for one of the four principal parties: Social Democratic Party (SDP), Centre Party (CP), People's Party (PP), and Conservatives (C). Those who abstained or voted for a minor party on any of the three occasions are omitted from the table. I am grateful to Professor B. Sarlvik for supplying these data.

In the table the parties have been arranged in their acknowledged left-wing to right-wing order. It is readily apparent that the majority (nearly 80 per cent) of the panel members remained loyal to a party throughout the study period. Closer scrutiny of the data reveals there is also a distance effect present; e.g. a defecting Social Democrat is more likely to switch allegiance to the Centre Party than to the more right-wing People's Party.

Table 10.7. Swedish voting data 1964, 1968, and 1970

1964 vote	1968 vote	1970 vote SDP	CP	PP	C	Total
SDP	SDP	812	27	16	5	860
	CP	5	20	6	0	31
	PP	2	3	4	0	9
	C	3	3	4	2	12
CP	SDP	21	6	1	0	28
	CP	3	216	6	2	227
	PP	0	3	7	0	10
	C	0	9	0	4	13
PP	SDP	15	2	8	0	25
	CP	1	37	8	0	46
	PP	1	17	157	4	179
	C	0	2	12	6	20
C	SDP	2	0	0	1	3
	CP	0	13	1	4	18
	PP	0	3	17	1	21
	C	0	12	11	126	149
Total		865	373	258	155	1651

The figures given in the table are in reality the cell frequencies of a three-dimensional $4 \times 4 \times 4$ table. The method of analysis depends on what is required. We shall take as our aim the formulation of a simple model to explain the 1970 voting figures. Denoting the votes of the panel on the three occasions to be the variables A, B, and C (in that chronological order), we shall treat A and B as factors and C as the single response variable. Each of these variables has categories numbered 1 to 4 corresponding to the four parties in the order they were presented.

Our basic model is the model of independence of the C variable on the A and B factors with the addition of the loyalty and distance effects noted earlier. For the distance effect we use the crossings variable S, as in equations (10.18). In our case we are comparing the 1968 and 1970 votes, and with four categories there are three distances involved. To cope with loyalty we introduce two dichotomous dummy variables X and Y. A cell belongs to category 1 of variable X if the 1964 and 1970 votes are identical and to category 2 otherwise; note that because X is dichotomous $\lambda_2^X = -\lambda_1^X$. Variable Y is similarly defined for the 1968 and 1970 votes. The entire model is then (somewhat loosely) written as

$$v_{ijk} = \mu + \lambda_i^A + \lambda_j^B + \lambda_{ij}^{AB} + \lambda_k^C + \sum \lambda_e^S \pm \lambda_1^X \pm \lambda_1^Y \qquad (10.19)$$

where $\sum \lambda_e^S$ refers to a sum over the relevant distances to get from j to k. The following example should clarify the model:

$$v_{424} = \mu + \lambda_4^A + \lambda_2^B + \lambda_{42}^{AB} + \lambda_4^C + \lambda_2^S + \lambda_3^S + \lambda_1^X - \lambda_1^Y$$

We can fit equation (10.19) either by the matrix approach of Section 8.5, or be treating the three distance parameters as dummy variables and expressing the complete $4 \times 4 \times 4$ table as an incomplete $4^3 \times 2^5$ table, or by expressing the model in multiplicative terms and using function maximization techniques.

The results of the model, which fits the data tolerably though not outstandingly ($\chi_{40}^2 = 55.2$), show that there was a swing to the centre in 1970, with the Centre Party being most popular, followed by the People's Party. However, because of the deterrent effects of distance and loyalty this does not mean that these were the parties gaining the most votes. Table 10.7 shows that the Social Democratic Party maintained a substantial majority in the panel, though the two centre Parties did have substantial gains in 1970. The parameter estimates reveal that (unsurprisingly) the two centre Parties appear closest together, with the largest gap being that between the Social Democratic and Centre Parties.

An interesting comparison is possible with two alternative simpler models, the pure loyalty and pure distance models obtained by dropping out either λ^S or λ^X and λ^Y from equation (10.19). These models both provide extremely poor explanations of the data ($\chi_{42}^2 = 312$ and $\chi_{43}^2 = 94$ respectively).

10.9. LATENT STRUCTURE MODELS

A completely different approach to the analysis of cross-classified data is based on the idea that the apparently complex relations that appear to exist between the variables in the cross-classification are explained by very simple relations between these variables and some other unobserved variables which are called *latent variables*.

To help with the understanding of the latent structure ideology, we return to the problem of finding a model for voting change. We saw that the mover–stayer model was naive and failed to provide a sensible explanation of the data. That model split the voters into two classes, movers and stayers; a sensible latent structure model would involve four (latent) classes. The latent class C consists of those voters whose basic philosophy is Conservative and who can be expected almost always—but not absolutely always—to vote Conservative. There would be corresponding classes S for Labour, L for Liberal, and A for Abstention. A person who votes Conservative on five consecutive occasions is almost surely a member of C, but *could* be a member of one of the other classes. The problems inherent with latent structure models lie in determining the probabilities of the various types of response for each of the classes, and indeed often—in less obvious situations—in determining how many underlying latent classes are necessary to explain the observed data. The essential feature of a latent class is that we cannot be sure that it exists!

The ideas of latent structure models are carefully set out by Lazarsfeld and Henry (1968) and are applied to panel analysis by Wiggins (1973). However, Wiggins ignores the statistical aspects of data variability and his approach relies on inspiration to produce a satisfactory model. Goodman (1974a, 1974b) has turned his attention to the latent structure model and with his usual thoroughness gives a detailed account of the necessary methodology utilizing log-linear models. In the remainder of this section we give an outline of his approach to the problem.

For illustrative purposes we suppose that we have a fourfold classification involving the variables A, B, C, and D, with p_{ijkl}^{ABCD} being the probability of an observation belonging to cell (i, j, k, l). According to the latent structure approach we hypothesize the existence of an observed (latent) variable X which has T classes. The number T is unknown and part of the analysis consists of discovering the effects of varying T and of judging what value of T is optimal. We now regard our data as constituting the $ABCD$ marginal totals of a five-way $ABCDX$ table. The same is true for the theoretical probabilities and in consequence we can write

$$p_{ijkl}^{ABCD} = \sum_{t=1}^{T} p_{ijklt}^{ABCDX} \qquad (10.20)$$

where p_{ijklt}^{ABCDX} is the (unknown) probability of an observation belonging to cell (i, j, k, l, t) of the five-way table.

It turns out that a convenient way of dealing with the latent variable X is to use quantities such as $p_{it}^{\bar{A}X}$, which is defined as the conditional probability of category i of variable A given the information that the relevant category of variable X is category t. Now, if within category t of variable X the variables A, B, C, and D are mutually independent, then we can write

$$p_{ijklt}^{ABCDX} = p_t^X p_{it}^{\bar{A}X} p_{jt}^{\bar{B}X} p_{kt}^{\bar{C}X} p_{lt}^{\bar{D}X} \qquad (10.21)$$

where p_t^X is the simple probability of an individual belonging to category t of variable X. If we were to take logarithms of the two sides of (10.21) then we would obtain a log-linear model of the basic independence type.

All the components of the right-hand side of equation (10.21) are unknown and need estimating. The maximum likelihood solutions are obtained by solving simultaneously equations such as the following:

$$n\hat{p}_t^X = \sum_i \sum_j \sum_k \sum_l f_{ijkl} \hat{p}_{ijklt}^{ABCD\bar{X}}$$

$$n\hat{p}_{it}^{\bar{A}X} \hat{p}_t^X = \sum_j \sum_k \sum_l f_{ijkl} \hat{p}_{ijklt}^{ABCD\bar{X}} \qquad (10.22)$$

where f_{ijkl} is the observed cell frequency, n is the total of all the cell frequencies, and the remaining terms are the maximum likelihood estimates of the corresponding probabilities. Solution of the equations is done numerically in an iterative fashion as described by Goodman, who states that convergence is fast.

The method is easily extended to cater for a number of latent variables. For example, if it is believed that there are two dichotomous latent variables Y and Z, then the previous theory can be used directly by taking X to have $2 \times 2 = 4$ categories and introducing suitable restrictions.

The latent structure idea whereby one or more latent variables are introduced which simplify apparently complex interrelations between the observed variables is very appealing. Goodman's examples show that very simple latent structure models perform marvellously well as explanations for previously intractable data sets. However, the number of possible latent structure models in terms of permutations of the numbers of latent variables and the numbers of categories for each of these variables is very great indeed; it would therefore seem wise only to consider using such models when one has some reasonably well-defined idea of the interpretation of the latent variables and preferably one has reason to surmise the existence of these latent variables in advance of an analysis of the data. The acid test, of course, is to use the latent structure model from one set of data on another set to which it might reasonably be expected to apply. Since the variables involved are necessarily invisible it is more than ordinarily imperative to be able to furnish convincing evidence of the appropriateness of the final model selected.

10.10. THE ANALYSIS OF PANEL DATA
EXHIBITING ATTRITION

We remarked in Section 9.8 that methods based on the usual maximum likelihood approach have been devised to deal with the problems of incomplete data of the sort where not all the categories of all the variables are known. A particularly acute form of this problem occurs automatically in any extended panel study—some panel members die or leave the panel for other reasons and new panel members are introduced. Over the complete duration of the panel there may be quite a considerable turnover of panel members with few remaining on the panel throughout its life.

Lehnen and Koch (1972, 1974b) study one such panel and set out in some detail an approach to the problem which enables them to obtain improved estimates of the parameters in their model by using the partial information on the temporary panel members as well as that from the permanent panel members. Their approach utilizes the extended least squares method of Grizzle, Starmer, and Koch (1969), which was briefly discussed in Section 8.5. The method they advocate includes tests to determine whether the temporary members differ significantly from the permanent members. Surprisingly their approach appears to be the only direct discussion of this problem in the literature to date.

10.11. EXTENSIONS OF THE MOVER–STAYER
MODEL AND RELATED IDEAS

Considerable efforts have been made to find extensions of the mover–stayer model with the analysis of social mobility in mind. The principal characteristics of this work are the development of some complex statistical theory divorced from examples of practical applications. The latter stricture must be tempered by noting that there appears to be little relevant data available on which to test these models. We note below some of the more recent work which, although principally concerned specifically with social mobility, could provide some useful clues in the development of the general analysis of panel data.

The mover–stayer model was formulated largely to 'explain' the large on-diagonal cell frequencies of the typical table. It has been recognized for some time that, as was demonstrated in Section 10.7, the model is unrealistically oversimplified. Ginsberg (1971) and Gilbert (1973) have extended the model using the 'law of cumulative inertia' stated by McGinnis (1968). This 'law' states that the longer a category (special class, job, voting allegiance) is occupied by an individual the less likely is that individual to change category. The Ginsberg–Gilbert work is based on the theory of semi-Markov processes, and relates the probability of a move between categories to both the category left and to the category entered. Spilerman (1973) suggests that instead of the two classes, movers and stayers, there should be a complete range of classes varying from the immobile to the ever-moving.

Reviews of recent developments in the study of social mobility are given by Singer and Spilerman (1974) and by Sorensen (1975).

Appendixes

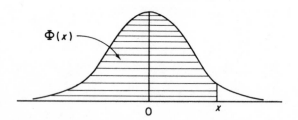

The normal distribution function

$\Phi(x) = P[X \le x]$, where X has a normal distribution with mean 0 and variance 1. (Note that if Z has a normal distribution with mean μ and variance σ^2, then $P[Z \le z] = \Phi[(z - \mu)/\sigma]$).

x	$\Phi(x)$	x	$\Phi(x)$
0.0	0.500	1.5	0.933
0.1	0.540	1.6	0.945
0.2	0.579	1.7	0.955
0.3	0.618	1.8	0.964
0.4	0.655	1.9	0.971
0.5	0.692	2.0	0.977
0.6	0.726	2.1	0.982
0.7	0.758	2.2	0.986
0.8	0.788	2.3	0.989
0.9	0.816	2.4	0.9918
1.0	0.841	2.5	0.9938
1.1	0.864	2.6	0.9953
1.2	0.885	2.7	0.9965
1.3	0.903	2.8	0.9974
1.4	0.919	2.9	0.9981

$$\Phi(-x) = 1 - \Phi(x)$$

134

APPENDIX 2

Percentage points of the chi-squared distribution

The figure in the table corresponding to the d row (d degrees of freedom) is that value, T, for which $P[\chi_d^2 > T] = P$, where P is the probability specified by the column heading.

Degrees of freedom d	Tail probability P			
	0.10	0.05	0.01	0.001
1	2.71	3.84	6.63	10.83
2	4.61	5.99	9.21	13.81
3	6.25	7.81	11.34	16.27
4	7.78	9.49	13.28	18.47
5	9.24	11.07	15.09	20.52
6	10.64	12.59	16.81	22.46
7	12.02	14.07	18.48	24.32
8	13.36	15.51	20.09	26.12
9	14.68	16.92	21.67	27.88
10	15.99	18.31	23.21	29.59
12	18.55	21.03	26.22	32.91
14	21.06	23.68	29.14	36.12
16	23.54	26.30	32.00	39.25
18	25.99	28.87	34.81	42.31
20	28.41	31.41	37.57	45.31
25	34.38	37.65	44.31	52.62
30	40.26	43.77	50.89	59.70
40	51.81	55.76	63.69	73.40
50	63.17	67.50	76.15	86.66
60	74.40	79.08	88.38	99.61
70	85.53	90.53	100.4	112.3
80	96.58	101.9	112.3	124.8
90	107.6	113.1	124.1	137.2
100	118.5	124.3	135.8	149.4
	10%	5%	1%	0.1%

REFERENCES

The list of references that follows comprises those mentioned in the text; the most complete source of references is Killian and Zahn (1976). The most comprehensive survey of the whole field of the analysis of cross-classified data which includes a considerable quantity of examples using real data is Bishop, Fienberg, and Holland (1975).

Acock, A. C. (1974). Measures of association for nominal data involving a theoretical prediction rule. *Pacific Soc. Rev.*, **17**, 240–248.

Altham, P. M. E. (1975). Quasi-independent triangular contingency tables. *Biometrics*, **31**, 233–238.

Anscombe, F. J. (1953). Contribution to discussion of paper by H. Hotelling 'New light on the correlation coefficient and its transform'. *J. Roy. Statist. Soc.*, B, **15**, 229–230.

Bahr, H. M. (1969). Institutional life, drinking and disaffiliation. *Social Problems*, **16**, 365–375.

Baker, R. J. (1977). Exact distributions derived from two-way tables. *Appl. Statist.*, **26**, 199–206.

Baptista, J., and Pike, M. C. (1977). Exact two-sided confidence limits for the odds ratio in a 2×2 table. *Appl. Statist.*, **26**, 214–220.

Bartlett, M. S. (1935). Contingency table interactions. *J. Roy. Statist. Soc. Suppl.*, **2**, 248–252.

Berkson, J. (1944). Application of the logistic function to bio-assay. *J. Amer. Statist. Assoc.*, **50**, 130–162.

Bhapkar, V. P., and Koch, G. G. (1968). On the hypothesis of 'no interaction' in multidimensional contingency tables. *Technometrics*, **10**, 107–124.

Birch, M. W. (1963). Maximum likelihood in three-way contingency tables. *J. Roy. Statist. Soc.*, B, **25**, 220–233.

Bishop, Y. M. M., and Fienberg, S. E. (1969). Incomplete two-dimensional contingency tables. *Biometrics*, **25**, 119–128.

Bishop, Y. M. M., Fienberg, S. E., and Holland, P. W. (1975). *Discrete Multivariate Analysis: Theory and Practice*, M.I.T. Press, Cambridge, Mass.

Blumen, I., Kogan, M., and McCarthy, P. J. (1955). *The Industrial Mobility of Labor as a Probability Process*. Cornell Studies of Industrial and Labor Relations, No. 6, Cornell University Press, Ithaca, New York.

Blyth, C. R. (1972). On Simpson's paradox and the sure-thing principle. *J. Amer. Statist. Assoc.* **67**, 364–366.

Bock, R. D. (1975). Multivariate analysis of qualitative data. In *Multivariate Statistical Methods in Behavioural Research*, McGraw-Hill, New York. Chap. 8.

Brown, M. B. (1976). Screening effects in multidimensional contingency tables. *Appl. Statist.*, **25**, 37–46.

Butler, D. E., and Stokes, D. E. (1975). *Political Change in Britain*, 2nd ed. Macmillan, London.

Chen, T., and Fienberg, S. E. (1974). Two-dimensional contingency tables with both completely and partially cross-classified data. *Biometrics*, **30**, 629–642.

Chen, T., and Fienberg, S. E. (1976). The analysis of contingency tables with incompletely classified data. *Biometrics*, **32**, 133–144.

Cochran, W. G. (1963). *Sampling Techniques*, 2nd ed. Wiley, New York.

Coleman, J. S. (1964). *Introduction to Mathematical Sociology*, Free Press, New York.

Conover, W. J. (1974). Some reasons for not using the Yates continuity correction on 2×2 contingency tables (with comments and rejoinder). *J. Amer. Statist. Assoc.*, **69**, 374–382.

Cornfield, J. (1956). A statistical problem arising from retrospective studies. In J. Neyman (Ed.), *Proc. Third Berkeley Symp.*, vol. IV, University of California Press, Berkeley, pp. 135–148.

Cox, D. R. (1972). The analysis of multivariate binary data. *Appl. Statist.*, **21**, 113–120.

Cox, D. R., and Lauh, E. (1967). A note on the graphical analysis of multidimensional contingency tables. *Technometrics*, **9**, 481–488.

Craddock, J. M., and Flood, C. R. (1970). The distribution of the χ^2 statistic in small contingency tables, *Appl. Statist.*, **19**, 173–181.

Crewe, I. (1976). Party identification theory and political change in Britain. In I. Budge, I. Crewe, and D. J. G. Farlie (Eds.), *Party Identification and Beyond*, Wiley, London.

Daniel, C. (1959). Use of half-normal plots in interpreting factorial two-level experiments. *Technometrics*, **1**, 311–341.

Davis, J. A. (1971). *Elementary Survey Analysis*, Prentice-Hall, Englewood Cliffs, N.J.

Davis, J. A. (1974). Hierarchical models for significance tests in multivariate contingency tables: an exegesis of Goodman's recent papers. In Herbert Costner (Ed.), *Sociological Methodology 1973–74*, Jossey-Bass, San Francisco, pp. 189–231.

Davis, J. A. (1976). Analyzing contingency tables with linear flow graphs: D systems. In D. R. Heise (Ed.), *Sociological Methodology 1976*, Jossey-Bass, San Francisco, pp. 111–145.

Deming, W. E., and Stephan, F. F. (1940). On a least squares adjustment of a sampled frequency table when the expected marginal totals are known. *Ann. Math. Statist.*, **11**, 427–444.

Draper, N. R., and Smith, H. (1966). *Applied Regression Analysis*, Wiley, New York.

Duncan, O. D. (1975). Partitioning polytomous variables in multiway contingency analysis. *Soc. Sci. Research*, **4**, 167–182.

Edwards, A. W. F. (1963). The measurement of association in a 2×2 table. *J. Roy. Statist. Soc.*, A, **126**, 109–114.

Fienberg, S. E. (1969). Preliminary graphical analysis and quasi-independence for two-way contingency tables. *Appl. Statist.*, **18**, 153–168.

Fienberg, S. E. (1970a). An iterative procedure for estimation in contingency tables. *Ann. Math. Statist.*, **41**, 907–917.

Fienberg, S. E. (1970b). Quasi-independence and maximum likelihood estimation in incomplete contingency tables. *J. Amer. Statist. Assoc.*, **65**, 1610–1616.

Fienberg, S. E. (1971). A statistical technique for historians: standardizing tables of counts. *J. Interdisciplinary History*, **1**, 305–315.

Fienberg, S. E. (1972). The analysis of incomplete multi-way contingency tables. *Biometrics*, **28**, 177–202.

Fienberg, S. E., and Holland, P. W. (1970). Methods for eliminating zero counts in contingency tables. In G. P. Patil (Ed.), *Random Counts in Models and Structures*, Pennsylvania State University Press, University Park.

Fienberg, S. E., and Holland, P. W. (1973). Simultaneous estimation of multinomial cell probabilities. *J. Amer. Statist. Assoc.*, **68**, 638–691.

Finney, D. J., Latscha, R., Bennett, B. M., and Hsu, P., with an introduction by Pearson, E. S. (1963). *Tables for Testing Significance in a 2 × 2 Contingency Table*, Cambridge University Press.

Fisher, R. A. (1962). Confidence limits for a cross-product ratio. *Aust. J. Statist.*, **4**, 41.

Gail, M. H. (1972). Mixed quasi-independent models for categorical data. *Biometrics*, **28**, 703–712.

Gart, J. J., and Thomas, D. G. (1972). Numerical results on approximate confidence limits for the odds ratio, *J. Roy. Statist. B*, **34**, 441–447.

Gart, J. J., and Zweifel, J. R. (1967). On the bias of various estimators of the logit and its variance. *Biometrika*, **54**, 181–187.

Gilbert, G. (1973). Semi-Markov processes and mobility: a note. *J. Math. Soc.*, **3**, 139–145.

Ginsberg, R. B. (1971). Semi-Markov processes and mobility. *J. Math. Soc.*, **1**, 233–262.

Goodman, L. A. (1968). The analysis of cross-classified data: independence, quasi-independence, and interactions in contingency tables with or without missing values. *J. Amer. Statist. Assoc.*, **63**, 1091–1131.

Goodman, L. A. (1969). On partitioning χ^2 and detecting partial association in three-way contingency tables. *J. Roy. Statist. Soc., B*, **31**, 486–498.

Goodman, L. A. (1970). The multivariate analysis of qualitative data: interactions among multiple classifications. *J. Amer. Statist. Assoc.*, **65**, 226–256.

Goodman, L. A. (1971a). The analysis of multidimensional contingency tables, step-wise procedures and direct estimation methods for building models for multiple classifications. *Technometrics*, **13**, 33–61.

Goodman, L. A. (1971b). Partitioning of chi-square, analysis of marginal contingency tables and estimation of expected frequencies in multidimensional contingency tables. *J. Amer. Statist. Assoc.*, **66**, 339–344.

Goodman, L. A. (1972a). A modified regression approach to the analysis of dichotomous variables. *Amer. Soc. Rev.*, **37**, 28–46.

Goodman, L. A. (1972b). A general model for the analysis of surveys. *Amer. J. Soc.*, **77**, 1035–1086.

Goodman, L. A. (1972c). Some multiplicative models for the analysis of cross-classified data. In L. LeCarn *et al.* (eds.), *Proc. Sixth Berkeley Symp. on Mathematical Statistics and Probability*, Vol. 1, University of California Press, Berkeley, pp. 649–696.

Goodman, L. A. (1973a). Causal analysis of data from panel studies and other kinds of surveys. *Amer. J. Soc.*, **78**, 1135–1191.

Goodman, L. A. (1973b). The analysis of multidimensional contingency tables when some variables are posterior to others: a modified path analysis approach. *Biometrika*, **60**, 179–192.

Goodman, L. A. (1974a). The analysis of systems of qualitative variables when some of the variables are unobservable, Part I—a modified latent structure approach. *Amer. J. Soc.*, **79**, 1179–1259.

Goodman, L. A. (1974b). Exploratory latent structure analysis using both identifiable and unidentifiable models. *Biometrika*, **61**, 215–231.

Goodman, L. A. (1976). The relationship between modified and usual multiple-regression approaches to the analysis of dichotomous variables. In D. R. Heise (Ed.), *Sociological Methodology 1976, Jossey-Bass, San Francisco, pp.* 83–110.

Goodman, L. A., and Fay, R. (1973). *Everyman's Contingency Table Analysis: Program Documentation*, University of Chicago Press, Chicago.

Goodman, L. A., and Kruskal, E. H. (1954), Measures of association for cross-classifications, I. *J. Amer. Statist. Assoc.*, **49**, 732–764.

Goodman, L. A., and Kruskal, E. H. (1963). Measures of association for cross-classifications, III. *J. Amer. Statist. Assoc.*, **58**, 310–364.

Goodman, L. A., and Kruskal, E. H. (1972). Measures of association for cross-classification, IV. *J. Amer. Statist. Assoc.*, **67**, 415–421.

Grizzle, J. E. (1967). Continuity correction in the χ^2-test for 2×2 tables. *American Statistician*, **21**, 4, 28–32.

Grizzle, J. E., Starmer, C. F., and Koch, G. G. (1969). Analysis of categorical data by linear models. *Biometrics*, **25**, 489–504.

Guttman, L. (1941). An outline of the statistical theory of prediction. In Paul Horst *et al.* (Eds.), *The Prediction of Personal Adjustment*, S.S.R.C., New York.

Haberman, S. J. (1972). Log-linear fit for contingency tables. *Appl. Statist.*, **21**, 218–225.

Haberman, S. J. (1973). The analysis of residuals in cross-classified tables. *Biometrics*, **29**, 205–220.

Haberman, S. J. (1974), Log-linear models for frequency tables with ordered classifications. *Biometrics*, **30**, 589–600.

Hocking, R. R. (1976). The analysis and selection of variables in linear regression. *Biometrics*, **32**, 1–49.

Hocking, R. R., and Oxspring, H. H. (1974). The analysis of partially categorized contingency data. *Biometrics*, **30**, 469–483.

Hornung, C. A., Gordon, R. A., Schmitt, R. L., Erickson, B., and Bayley, C. (1975). Commentary and debate on Hunter's article on the validity of measures of association (with reply by the author). *Amer. J. Soc.*, **80**, 975–1002.

Hunter, A. A. (1974). On the validity of measures of association: the nominal–nominal, two-by-two case. *Amer. J. Soc.*, **79**, 99–109.

Ireland, C. T., Ku, H. H., and Kullback, S. (1969). Symmetry and marginal homogeneity of an $r \times r$ contingency table. *J. Amer. Statist. Assoc.*, **64**, 1323–1341.

Kastenbaum, M. A. (1974). Analysis of categorical data: some well-known analogues and some new concepts. *Comm. Statist.*, **3**, 401–417.

Kendall, M. G., and Stuart, A. (1973). *The Advanced Theory of Statistics*: Vol. 2, *Inference and Relationships*, Griffin, London.

Killian, R. A., and Zahn, D. A. (1976). A bibliography of contingency table literature. *Int. Stat. Rev.*, **44**, 71–112.

Knoke, D. (1975). A comparison of log-linear and regression models for systems of dichotomous variables. *Soc. Methods and Research*, **3**, 416–434.

Koch,. G. G., Imrey, P. B., and Reinfurt, D. W. (1972). Linear model analysis of categorical data with incomplete response vectors. *Biometrics*, **28**, 663–692.

Kruskal, W. H. (1958). Ordinal measures of association. *J. Amer. Statist. Assoc.*, **53**, 814–861.

Ku, H. H., and Kullback, S. (1968). Interaction in multidimensional contingency tables: an information theoretic approach. *J. Res. Nat. Bur. Standards Sect.*, **72**, 159–199.

Ku, H. H., Varner, R. N., and Kullback, S. (1971). Analysis of multidimensional contingency tables. *J. Amer. Statist. Assoc.*, **66**, 55–64.

Lazarsfeld, P. F., and Henry, N. W. (1968). *Latent Structure Analysis*, Houghton-Griffin, Boston.

Leathers, B. L. (1977). Computing the numerator of ordinal measures of association when the data are ordered categories, *Appl. Statist.*, **26**, 211–213.

Lehnen, R. G., and Koch, G. G. (1972). The stability of voter preferences in two southern states: an analysis of panel data with attrition. *Proc. Amer. Statist. Assoc.*, **1972**, 352–355.

Lehnen, R. G., and Koch, G. G. (1974a). A general linear approach to the analysis of nonmetric data: applications for political science. *Amer. J. Pol. Sci.*, **18**, 283–313.

Lehnen, R. G., and Koch, G. G. (1974b). Analyzing panel data with uncontrolled attrition. *Public Opinion Quarterly*, **38**, 40–56.

Lindley, D. V., and Miller, J. C. P. (1952). *Cambridge Elementary Statistical Tables*, Cambridge University Press.

McGinnis, R. (1968). A stochastic model of social mobility. *Amer. Soc. Rev.*, **73**, 712–722.

Mackerras, M. (1970). *D.L.P. Preference Distribution 1959–1969*. Occasional Monograph No. 3, Dept. of Government and Public Administration, University of Sydney.

Mantel, N. (1969). Models for complex contingency tables and polychotomous dosage response curves. *Biometrics*, **22**, 83–95.

Maxwell, A. E. (1961). *Analyzing Qualitative Data*, Methuen, London.

Mosteller, F. (1968). Association and estimation in contingency tables. *J. Amer. Statist. Assoc.* **63**, 1–28.

Nelder, J. A. (1974). Log-linear models for contingency tables: a generalisation of classical least squares. *Appl. Statist.*, **23**, 323–329.

Nie, N. H., Hull, C. H., Jenkins, J. G., Steinbrenner, K., and Bent, D. H. (1975). *Statistical Package for the Social Sciences*, 2nd ed., McGraw-Hill, New York.

Pearson, E. S., and Hartley, H. O. (Eds.) (1966). *Biometrika Tables for Statisticians*, Vol. 1, 3rd ed. Cambridge University Press.

Pearson, K. (1904). On the theory of contingency and its relation to association and normal correlation. *Draper's Co. Res. Mem. Biometric Ser. I*, reprinted (1948) in *Karl Pearson's Early Papers*, Cambridge University Press.

Plackett, R. L. (1962). A note on interactions in contingency tables. *J. Roy. Statist. Soc.*, *B*, **24**, 162–166.

Plackett, R. L. (1974). *The Analysis of Categorical Data*, Griffin, London.

Roy, S. N., and Kastenbaum, M. A. (1956). On the hypothesis of 'no interaction' in a multi-way contingency table. *Ann. Math. Statist.*, **27**, 749–757.

Simpson, E. H. (1951). The interpretation of interaction in contingency tables. *J. Roy. Statist. Soc.*, *B*, **13**, 238–241.

Singer, B., and Spilerman, S. (1974). Social mobility models for heterogeneous populations. In Herbert Costner (Ed.), *Sociological Methodology, 1973–74*, Jossey-Bass, San Francisco, pp. 356–401.

Smith, K. W. (1976). Marginal standardisation and table shrinking: aids in the traditional analysis of contingency tables. *Social Forces*, **59**, 669–693.

Somers, R. H. (1962). A new asymmetric measure of association for ordinal variables. *Amer. Soc. Rev.*, **27**, 799–811.

Sorensen, A. B. (1975). Models for social mobility. *Soc. Sci. Research*, **4**, 65–92.

Spilerman, S. (1973). Extensions of the mover–stayer model. *Amer. J. Soc.*, **78**, 599–626.

Theil, H. (1971). On the estimation of relationships involving qualitative variables. *Amer. J. Soc.*, **76**, 103–154.

Thomas, D. G. (1971). Exact limits for the odds ratio in a 2×2 table. *Appl. Statist.*, **20**, 105–110.

Upton, G. J. G. (1977). A memory model for voting transitions in British Elections. *J. Roy. Statist. Soc.*, *A*, **140**, 86–94.

Wagner, S. E. (1970). The maximum-likelihood estimate for contingency tables with zero diagonal. *J. Amer. Statist. Assoc.*, **65**, 1362–1383.

Wiggins, L. M. (1973). *Panel Analysis*, Elsevier, Amsterdam.

Williams, D. A. (1976). Improved likelihood-ratio tests for complete contingency tables. *Biometrika*, **63**, 33–38.

Williams, O. D., and Grizzle, J. E. (1972). Analysis of contingency tables having ordered response categories. *J. Amer. Statist. Assoc.*, **67**, 55–63.

Yarnold, J. K. (1970). The minimum expectation in χ^2 goodness-of-fit tests and the accuracy of approximation for the null distribution. *J. Amer. Statist. Assoc.*, **65**, 864–886.

Yates, F. (1934). Contingency tables involving small numbers and the Chi-square test. *J. Roy. Statist. Soc. Suppl.*, **1**, 217–235.

Yeomans, K. A. (1968). *Statistics for the Social Scientist: 2. Applied Statistics*, Penguin Books, Harmondsworth.

Yule, G. U. (1900). On the association of attributes in statistics. *Phil. Trans.*, A, **194**, 257–319.

Zahn, D. A. (1975). Modifications of and revised critical values for the half-normal plot. *Technometrics*, **17**, 189–200.

Author Index

Subject Index